Zoology 3 Notebooking Journal

for

Exploring Creation with Zoology 3: Land Animals

by
Jeannie Fulbright

Exploring Creation with Zoology 3
Notebooking Journal

Published by
Apologia Educational Ministries, Inc.
P.O. Box 896844
Charlotte, NC, 28289-6844
apologia.com

ISBN: 978-1-935495-13-0

Cover Design by Kim Williams

All biblical quotations are from the *New American Standard Bible, King James Version, New International Version*, or *New King James Version*

Printed by Bradford & Bigelow, Newburyport, MA
January 2022

20 19 18 17 16 15 14 13

Photo Credits

All photos are licensed from Jupiter Images except the following:
Images by Crestock: 73, A5, A9, A13, A14, A15, A16, A17, A18, A19, A21, A23, A25, A33, A35, A37, A39, A41, A45, A49, A51, A53, A55, A57, A59, A61 MAP IT: Skunk, Lion, Tiger, Lynx, Striped Hyena, Koala, Sugar Glider, Chimpanzee, Baboon, Macaque, Lemur, Rat, Sloth, Armadillo, Anteater, Donkey, Zebra, Rhino, Impala. Wildebeest, Gazelle, Giraffe, Gecko, Chameleon
Wikipedia Commons: Raccoon Dog, Jackal, Sun Bear, Sea Otter, Brown Hyena, Aardwolf, Wombat, Possum, Tasmanian Devil, Opossum, Mandrill, Proboscis Monkey, Tamarin, Marmoset, Flying Squirrel, Platypus, Squamates, Tortoise, Alligator
Norman Lim, Naional University of Singapore: Colugo
AnimalsAnimals.com: MAP IT: Aye-Aye
Images by Kim Williams: A1

Fonts used with permission/license from:

Myfonts.com: Otto Maurer - Turtle Black Shadow; Nick's Fonts - Cool Cat Jim; Larabie product - Ennobled Pet; TypeSETit - Mo Lah Lah; CheapProFonts - Kingthings Willow Pro; Sideshow - Bamboozle; Intellecta Designs - Intellecta Borders, Bailarina; Scriptorium - Morris Initials; Scholtz Fonts - GiraffeSkin, Leoopard Skin, Zebra Skin; Gerald Gallo - Make Tracks; ARTypes - Maria Balle Initials; FontHaus - Novella; Studiocharlie - Superstarlike; HiH - Waltari; Typgrapher Mediengestaltung - Airmole; BrainEaters Font Co.-Musicals; Adobe - Critter Std., Bermuda
Linotype: Animalia, Zapfino
Educational Fontware: Abeka Cursive, HWT
Will-Harris: Daylilies; Isis-Font: Lost World; Gulash - Ginger Snake

Note from the Author

Welcome to the wonderful adventure in learning called "Notebooking." This notebooking journal correlates with Apologia's *Exploring Creation with Zoology 3,* by Jeannie Fulbright. The activities in this journal provide everything your child needs to complete the assignments in *Exploring Creation with Zoology 3* and more. It will serve as your child's individual notebook. You only need to provide scissors, glue, colored pencils, a stapler and a few brass fasteners.

The concept of notebooking is not a new one. In fact, keeping notebooks was the primary way the learned men of our past educated themselves, from Leonardo Da Vinci and Christopher Columbus to George Washington, John Quincy Adams and Meriwether Lewis. These men and many others of their time were avid notebookers. As we know, they were also much more advanced in their knowledge—even as teens—than we are today. George Washington was a licensed surveyor during his teenage years, and John Quincy Adams graduated from law school at age 17.

It would be wise for us to emulate the methods of education of these great men, rather than the failing methods used in our schools today. Common modern methods, namely fill-in-the-blank and matching worksheets, do not fully engage the student's mind. Studies show that we remember only 5% of what we hear, 50% of what we see and hear and 90% of what we see, hear and do. When we participate in activities that correspond with learning, we increase our retention exponentially. This is exactly what the Zoology 3 Notebooking Journal is designed to do—offer engaging learning activities to increase your student's retention.

The National Center for Educational Statistics shows us that American school children, by twelfth grade, rank at the bottom of international assessments, and do not even know 50% of what students in top-ranked countries know. As home educators, we have the opportunity to discard methods that are detrimental and ineffective and adopt the methods which will genuinely educate our children.

In addition to academic achievement, notebooking offers many benefits to students and parents. For students, it provides an opportunity to uniquely express themselves as they learn. It also provides a treasured memento of educational endeavors. For parents, it is a record of the year's studies and can easily be transferred to a portfolio if needed.

This journal will make notebooking easier for both you and your student by supplying a plethora of templates, hands-on crafts and projects, additional experiment ideas, and many activities that will engage your student in learning. It will prove invaluable in helping students create a wonderful keepsake of all they learned in zoology 3. Remember that *everything in this notebooking journal is optional.* Because it will serve as your student's own unique notebook, you may customize it by simply tearing out the activity pages that you choose not to use. You, as the teacher, will decide what truly benefits your student's learning experience, encourages a love for learning and builds his confidence in science. Every child is different, learns differently and will respond differently to the array of activities provided here. Use discernment in how many of the activities and assignments you use with your child. Your goal is not to complete every activity but to make learning a joy.

However, as a seasoned home educator, let me encourage you not to attempt to do every single activity in this note-booking journal. Choose the projects and activities that will be enjoyable and inspire a love of learning. If something is a drudgery, it will not serve to increase your student's retention, but will only discourage his enjoyment of science—resulting in an unmotivated learner.

It is my hope and prayer that you and your students will benefit from your studies this year, growing closer to God as you learn of His creation, and finding joy in the learning process.

Warmly,

3

Table of Contents

Table of Contents

Zoology 3 Notebooking Journal

Below are descriptions of a suggested schedule and the activities included in this notebooking journal. The first five activities are taken directly from the coursework contained in *Exploring Creation with Zoology 3*. The others are additional optional activities coordinating with the book.

Suggested Schedule

A suggested schedule for reading the *Exploring Creation with Zoology 3* text and completing the activities contained in the book and in this journal has been provided. Though not every student or parent will choose to utilize the schedule, those who do may find it very beneficial. Some parents will appreciate having their student's daily reading and assignments organized for them. Older students will find it easy to complete the book and journal by following the schedule on their own. Though the suggested schedule provides for the zoology course to be completed in twenty-eight weeks, two days per week, it is flexible and can be made to fit your goals. The course can be expedited by completing three or four days of science per week. You can lengthen the course by studying science only one day per week. If you wish to do the extra activities found in the Explore More pages, still another day of science can be added. Above all, use the suggested schedule in a way that best suits your family.

Fascinating Facts

Exploring Creation with Zoology 3 contains many facts, ideas and interesting notions. Although oral (verbal) narration is an effective means for retention, your student may wish to record some of the information either through drawing or writing. The Fascinating Facts pages can be used for written narrations. Some of the lessons provide two Fascinating Facts pages for your student's use. If your student is an avid writer, you can access more Fascinating Facts pages to print (free of charge) on the Apologia website. To do so, simply login to www.apologia.com/bookextras and type in this password: godmadethemcrawl. These additional pages can be included in this notebooking journal by simply stapling them onto one of the existing Fascinating Facts pages.

What Do You Remember? Review Questions

These review questions are the same questions asked in the "What Do You Remember?" section found in each lesson of the book. They can be answered orally (verbally) or, for older students, as a written narration assignment. For co-ops or classroom use, these questions may also serve as a way to evaluate how much the students have retained from the reading. However, I would encourage you to review the material with the students before giving the questions as a written narration assignment. This will encourage better retention of the material and increase both the students' confidence and their ability to restate their learning. The answers to the review questions can be found on pages 267 through 271 of *Exploring Creation with Zoology 3*.

Notebooking Assignments, Activities and Projects

The lessons in *Exploring Creation with Zoology 3* offer suggested notebooking assignments, activities and projects typically found at the end of each lesson. Provided in this journal are templates (blank pages with lines for writing or space for drawing) which your student can use for completing these activities. Colored pencils can be used to encourage creative, high quality work. Some projects require the student to use a Scientific Speculation Sheet. These sheets have been included in this notebooking journal. Drawings or pictures of the projects can be pasted onto the Scientific Speculation Sheets.

Map It! and Track It!

In the appendix of this notebooking journal you will find animal images to complete the Map It! activities contained in the text. You will only need to provide a large wall map. Instructions for completing the Map It! activities can be found at the end of the lessons.

Many lessons will have a Track It! activity designed to encourage your students to find and record different animal tracks. Templates for creating an animal tracks book are provided on page 247, in the section of this journal before the cut and fold miniature books. Simply tear these pages from the journal and fold and staple them to create a book. Instructions for completing the Track It! activities can be found at the end of the lessons. More Track It! pages are available on the course website to download and print if your student finds he needs more.

Scripture Copywork

Incorporating the Word of God in your science studies through Scripture Copywork will provide many benefits to your student. It will encourage stronger faith and memorization of Scripture, as well as better writing, spelling and grammar skills. Each lesson has a corresponding verse for your child to copy, which may be printed or written in cursive.

Vocabulary Crosswords

If you desire to expand your child's studies with vocabulary activities, the Vocabulary Crosswords can be used to review the new words and concepts mentioned in the lesson. Remember, working with the vocabulary in this manner is not a "test" of your child's knowledge, but should be viewed as a reinforcement and reminder of what he has learned. The answers to the Vocabulary Crosswords can be found on pages 240 through 243.

Project Pages

Many of the projects and experiments in *Exploring Creation with Zoology 3* are "hands-on" and therefore cannot be preserved in a notebook. Each lesson in this notebooking journal provides a Project Page in which your student can write about what he did and learned from the various projects and experiments contained in the coursework. Be sure to take pictures of the finished products and glue them onto the Project Pages. Your child will enjoy looking back and remembering the fun he had learning zoology 3!

Cut and Fold Miniature Books

At the back of this journal, you will find Cut and Fold Miniature Book craft activities that correspond with the reading. These miniature books are designed to review the concepts learned in each lesson. Writing lines are provided on the miniature books so your students can record the information they have learned. Some books ask for specific information. Others do not and allow the students to record the facts they found most interesting. Students will cut out the pattern, write what they have learned in the designated places, then assemble the books according to the directions. Paste Pages are included in this journal for each miniature book activity. The Paste Pages provide a place for your students to preserve and display their Cut and Fold Miniature Books. Instructions are included for pasting the miniature books onto the Paste Pages.

These books are entirely optional. Some students thrive with the hands-on approach, while other students do not benefit academically from this type of activity. Allow your students to try the Cut and Fold Miniature Books to see if they enjoy learning in this way.

Explore More

The Explore More suggestions are designed to give your student additional ideas and activities that might enhance his studies such as: experiments, hands-on activities, research and living book titles, as well as audio and video resources. Because these assignments are entirely optional, they are not included in the suggested schedule for completing the notebooking journal.

Field Trip Sheets

Your family may wish to further enhance your studies by visiting a zoo or science museum. Field Trip Sheets are provided at the back of this notebooking journal to record your visits. You can make a pocket on the back of these sheets to hold any brochures or additional information you receive. Simply glue three edges (sides and bottom) of a half piece of construction paper to the bottom of the Field Trip Sheet.

Final Review

At the end of this journal are 50 questions that review the entire course. They can be answered orally or in writing. This is an optional activity; however, I believe your students would be pleasantly surprised to see how much they know about zoology 3 after answering the questions. The answers to the Final Review can be found on page 244.

Week	Day 1	Day 2
1	**Lesson 1 - Animals of Day Six** Read *T pp. 1-4* & Narrate Begin working on Fascinating Facts about Zoology *NJ p. 12* Read *T pp. 4-6* & Narrate	Read *T pp. 6-8* & Narrate Read *T pp. 8-11* & Narrate
2	**Lesson 1 - Animals of Day Six** Written Narration: What Do You Remember? *T p. 11, NJ p. 14* Map It! and Track It! *T p. 11* Notebooking Activity: Animal Careers and Predator and Prey Drawing *T p. 12, NJ p. 15*	Scripture Copywork *NJ p. 16* Vocabulary Crossword *NJ p. 18* Zoology Minibook *NJ Appendix p. A 7* Experiment: Camouflaged Animals *T p. 12, NJ p. 23*
3	**Lesson 2 - Carnivorous Mammals** Read *T pp. 15-18* & Narrate Begin working on Fascinating Facts about Carnivorous Mammals *NJ p. 24* Try This! *T p. 18*	Read *T pp. 18-21* & Narrate Read *T pp. 21-23* & Narrate Read *T pp. 24-28* & Narrate
4	**Lesson 2 - Carnivorous Mammals** Written Narration: What Do You Remember? *T p. 28, NJ p. 26* Map It! and Track It! *T p. 29* Notebooking Activity: Canine Newsletter *T p. 29, NJ p. 27*	Scripture Copywork *NJ p. 28* Vocabulary Crosswords *NJ p. 30* Carnivorous Mammals Minibook *NJ p. A 9* Experiment: A Person's Sense of Smell *T p. 30, NJ p. 38*
5	**Lesson 3 - Caniforms Continued** Read *T pp. 31-35* & Narrate Begin working on Fascinating Facts about Caniforms *NJ p. 39* Try This! *T p. 35*	Read *T pp. 36-39* & Narrate Read *T pp. 39-41* & Narrate Try This! *T p. 41* Read *T pp. 41-44* & Narrate
6	**Lesson 3 -Caniforms Continued** Read *T pp. 44-49* & Narrate Written Narration: What Do You Remember? *T p. 49, NJ p. 40* Notebooking Activity: Different Families *T p. 49, NJ p. 41* Notebooking Activity: Bear Comic Strip *T p. 49, NJ p. 43*	Map It! and Track It! *T p. 49-50* Scripture Copywork *NJ p. 44* Vocabulary Crosswords *NJ p. 46* Caniforms Minibook *NJ Appendix A 13* Experiment: Which Color Gets Hotter? *T p. 50, NJ p. 51*
7	**Lesson 4 - Feliform Carnivores** Read *T pp. 51-54* & Narrate Begin working on Fascinating Facts about Feliform Carnivores *NJ p. 52* Read *T pp. 54-58* & Narrate	Try This! *T p. 58* Read *T pp. 58-60* & Narrate Try This! *T p. 60* Read *T pp. 60-64* & Narrate
8	**Lesson 4 - Feliform Carnivores** Read *T pp. 64-67* & Narrate Written Narration: What Do You Remember? *T p. 67, NJ p. 55* Map It! and Track It! *T p. 68* Notebooking Activity: Storyboard *T p. 68, NJ p. 56* Notebooking Activity: Feliform Fact Sheets *T p. 68, NJ p. 58*	Scripture Copywork *NJ p. 60* Vocabulary Crosswords *NJ p. 62* Feliforms Minibook *NJ Appendix p. A 19* Experiment: The Cougar Eats the Deer *T p. 69, NJ pp. 69-70*
9	**Lesson 5 - Marsupials** Read *T pp. 71-73* & Narrate Begin working on Fascinating Facts about Marsupials *NJ p. 71* Try This! Pangea *T p. 73, NJ p.73* Read *T pp. 73-74* & Narrate	Try This! *T p. 74* Read *T pp. 75-78* & Narrate Read *T pp. 79-82* & Narrate Read *T pp. 82-86* & Narrate
10	**Lesson 5 - Marsupials** Written Narration: What Do You Remember? *T p. 86, NJ p. 76* Map It! and Track It! *T p. 86-87* Notebooking Activity: Venn Diagram *T p. 87, NJ p. 77* Notebooking Activity: Marsupial Pages *T p. 87, NJ p. 78*	Scripture Copywork *NJ p. 80* Vocabulary Crosswords *NJ p. 82* Marsupials Minibook *NJ Appendix p. A 23* Project: Animal Tracks *T p. 87, NJ p. 89*
11	**Lesson 6 - Primarily Primates** Read *T pp. 89-94* & Narrate Begin working on Fascinating Facts About Primates *NJ p. 90* Begin Primates Classification Chart *T p. 94, NJ p. 92*	Read *T pp. 95-98* & Narrate Read *T pp. 98-100* & Narrate Read *T pp. 100-103* & Narrate

*Page numbers for the zoology text are indicated by *T p*. Page numbers for the notebooking journal are indicated by *NJ p*.

Week	Day 1	Day 2
12	**Lesson 6 - Primarily Primates** Read *T pp. 104-109* & Narrate Written Narration: What Do You Remember? *T p. 109, NJ p. 93* Map It! *T p. 109* Notebooking Activity: Travel Brochure *T p. 109, NJ p.95* Notebooking Activity: Primates Classification *T p. 110, NJ p. 92*	Scripture Copywork *NJ p. 100* Vocabulary Crosswords *NJ p. 102* Primates Minibook *NJ Appendix p. A 25* Experiment: Depth Perception *T p. 110*
13	**Lesson 7 - Rodentia and the Rest** Read *T pp. 111-114* & Narrate Begin working on Fascinating Facts about Rodentia *NJ p. 109* Read *T pp. 114-118* & Narrate	Read *T pp. 118-122* & Narrate Try This! *T p. 122* Read *T pp. 122-127* & Narrate Try This! *T p. 127*
14	**Lesson 7 - Rodentia and the Rest** Read *T pp. 127-128* & Narrate Written Narration: What Do You Remember? *T p. 129, NJ p. 110* Map It! and Track It! *T p. 129* Notebooking Activity: Creature Facts *T p. 129, NJ p. 111*	Notebooking Activity: Create a Creature *T p. 130, NJ p. 117* Scripture Copywork *NJ p. 118* Vocabulary Crosswords *NJ p. 120* Rodentia Minibook *NJ Appendix A 29* Experiment: Examine the Bones of a Rodent *T p. 130*
15	**Lesson 8 - Ungulates** Read *T pp. 131-134* & Narrate Begin working on Fascinating Facts about Ungulates *NJ p. 128* Read *T pp. 135-137* & Narrate	Read *T pp. 137-140* & Narrate Read *T pp. 140-142* & Narrate Read *T pp. 143-146* & Narrate Read *T pp. 146-148* & Narrate
16	**Lesson 8 - Ungulates** Written Narration: What Do You Remember? *T p. 149, NJ p. 129* Map It! and Track It! *T p. 149* Notebooking Activity: Creature Facts *T p. 149, NJ p. 130* Notebooking Activity: Odd-Toed Ungulates *T p. 149, NJ p. 135*	Scripture Copywork *NJ p. 136* Vocabulary Crosswords *NJ p. 138* Ungulates Minibook *NJ Appendix p. A 33* Review Game *T p. 149*
17	**Lesson 9 - Order Artiodactyla** Read *T pp. 151-155 & Narrate* Begin working on Fascinating Facts about Artiodactyla *NJ p. 146* Try This! *T p. 155*	Read *T pp. 155-158* & Narrate Try This! *T p. 158* Read *T pp. 158-162* & Narrate Read *T pp. 163-166* & Narrate
18	**Lesson 9 - Order Artiodactyla** Read *T pp. 166-169* & Narrate Written Narration: What Do You Remember? *T p. 169, NJ p. 148* Map It! and Track It! *T p. 169* Notebooking Activity: *Design a Zoo T p. 169, NJ p. 149*	Scripture Copywork *NJ p. 150* Vocabulary Crosswords *NJ p. 152* Artiodactyls Minibook *NJ Appendix p. A 39* Experiment: A Giraffe's Blood Pressure *T p. 170*
19	**Lesson 10 - Orders Squamata and Rhynchocephalia** Read *T pp. 171-174* & Narrate Begin working on Fascinating Facts about Squamates and Tuataras *NJ p. 160* Read *T pp. 174-178* & Narrate	Read *T pp. 179-182* & Narrate Read *T pp. 182-185* & Narrate
20	**Lesson 10 - Orders Squamata and Rhynchocephalia** Read *T pp. 186-189* & Narrate Written Narration: What Do You Remember? *T p. 189, NJ p. 163* Map It! and Track It! *T p. 189* Notebooking Activity: Venn Diagram *T p. 190, NJ p. 164* Notebooking Activity: Special Snake Abilities *T p. 190, NJ p. 164*	Notebooking Activity: Lizard Facts *T p. 190, NJ p. 165* Notebooking Activity: Tuatara Speech *T p. 190, NJ p. 166* Project: Venomous Snakes in my Area *T p. 190, NJ p. 167* Scripture Copywork *NJ p. 168* Vocabulary Crosswords *NJ p. 170* Squamates Minibooks *NJ Appendix p. A 41* Project *T p. 190, NJ p. 176*

*Page numbers for the zoology text are indicated by *T p.* Page numbers for the notebooking journal are indicated by *NJ p.*

Week	Day 1	Day 2
21	**Lesson 11 - The Rest of the Reptiles and Amphibians** Read *T pp. 191-193* & Narrate Begin working on Fascinating Facts about Reptiles and Amphibians *NJ p. 177* Read *T pp. 194-197* & Narrate	Read *T pp. 197-201* & Narrate Read *T pp. 201-206* & Narrate Read *T pp. 207-209* & Narrate
22	**Lesson 11 - The Rest of the Reptiles and Amphibians** Written Narration: What Do You Remember? *T p. 209, NJ p. 178* Map It! and Track It! *T p. 209* Notebooking Activity: Venn Diagram *T p. 210, NJ p. 179* Notebooking Activity: Testudines, Crocodilians and Amphibians *T p. 210, NJ p. 180*	Notebooking Activity: Amphibian Diary *T p. 210, NJ p. 183* Scripture Copywork *NJ p. 184* Vocabulary Crosswords *NJ p. 186* Herps Minibook *NJ Appendix p. A 41* Project: Keeping a Turtle *T p. 210, NJ p. 193*
23	**Lesson 12 - Dinosaurs** Read *T pp. 211-214* & Narrate Begin working on Fascinating Facts about Dinosaurs *NJ p. 194* Read *T pp. 215-217* & Narrate	Read *T pp. 217-218* & Narrate Try This! *T p. 219* Read *T pp. 219-223* & Narrate
24	**Lesson 12 - Dinosaurs** Read *T pp. 224-226* & Narrate Written Narration: What Do You Remember? *T p. 226, NJ p. 196* Map It! and Track It! *T p. 227* Notebooking Activity: Dinosaur Pages *T p. 227, NJ p. 197*	Scripture Copywork *NJ p. 200* Vocabulary Crossword *NJ p. 202* Dinosaurs Minibooks *NJ Appendix p. A 47* Experiment: Reptile Models *T p. 227, NJ p. 207*
25	**Lesson 13 - Arthropods of the Land** Read *T pp. 229-232* & Narrate Begin working on Fascinating Facts about Arthropods *NJ p. 208* Read *T pp. 232-234* & Narrate	Try This! *T p. 234* Read *T pp. 234-238* & Narrate Mid-lesson Notebooking Activity: Spider Web Hunt *T p. 238, NJ p. 209* Mid-lesson Project: Create a Web Frame *T p. 238, NJ p. 211* Read *T pp. 239-243* & Narrate
26	**Lesson 13 - Arthropods of the Land** Read *T pp. 243-247* & Narrate Written Narration: What Do You Remember? *T p. 247, NJ p. 210* Notebooking Activity: Searching for Arthropods *T p. 247, NJ p. 211* Notebooking Activity: Interesting Arthropods *T p. 247, NJ 212*	Scripture Copywork *NJ p. 214* Vocabulary Crosswords *NJ p. 216* Arthropods Minibook *NJ Appendix p. A 49* Experiment: Woodlouse Population Study *T p. 247, NJ p. 223*
27	**Lesson 14 - Gastropods and Worms** Read *T pp. 249-251* & Narrate Begin working on Fascinating Facts about Gastropods and Worms *NJ p. 224* Try This! *T p. 251*	Read *T pp. 251-255* & Narrate Read *T pp. 255-258* & Narrate Read *T pp. 258-262* & Narrate Try This! *T p. 262*
28	**Lesson 14 - Gastropods and Worms** Read *T pp. 262-265* & Narrate Try This! *T p. 265* Written Narration: What Do You Remember? *T p. 266, NJ p. 226* Notebooking Activity: Gastropods *T p. 266, NJ p. 227* Notebooking Activity: Tapeworms *T p. 266, NJ p. 228* Notebooking Activity: Earthworms *T p. 266, NJ p. 229*	Scripture Copywork *NJ p. 230* Vocabulary Crossword *NJ p. 232* Gastropods and Worms Minibook *NJ Appendix p. A 55* Experiment: Worm Temperature Preference *T p. 266, NJ p. 237*

*Page numbers for the zoology text are indicated by *T p.* Page numbers for the notebooking journal are indicated by *NJ p.*

This journal belongs to:

Isaac King

FASCINATING FACTS

ABOUT

ZOOLOGY

LESSON 1

today we will
be talking about
Day 6 of gods
creation

if you have ever gone on a safari you
will see gods amazing work
from lions, tigers, and so much
more if you happing to be a zooaligis
are know one you will know zoology

is the study
of anamols,
and that what
we will be lea-
rning about

FASCINATING FACTS

ABOUT

ZOOLOGY

LESSON 1

What Do You Remember?
Lesson 1 Review Questions

1. Explain what animal habituation is.

2. What is a safari?

3. What does it mean to be a predator?

4. What does it mean to be prey?

5. Have there always been predators and prey?

6. What is a zoonotic disease?

7. Name a few careers that involve working with animals.

PREDATOR AND PREY

"And the wolf will dwell with the lamb, and the leopard will lie down with the young goat, and the calf and the young lion and the fatling together; and a little boy will lead them. Also the cow and the bear will graze, their young will lie down together, and the lion will eat straw like the ox. The nursing child will play by the hole of the cobra, and the weaned child will put his hand on the viper's den. They will not hurt or destroy in all My holy mountain."

Isaiah 11:6-9

And God said, "Let the land produce living creatures according to their kinds: livestock, creatures that move along the ground, and wild animals, each according to its kind." And it was so.

Genesis 1:24

And God said, "Let the land produce living creatures according to their kinds: livestock, creatures that move along the ground, and wild animals, each according to its kind." And it was so.

Genesis 1:24

Vocabulary Crossword
Lesson 1

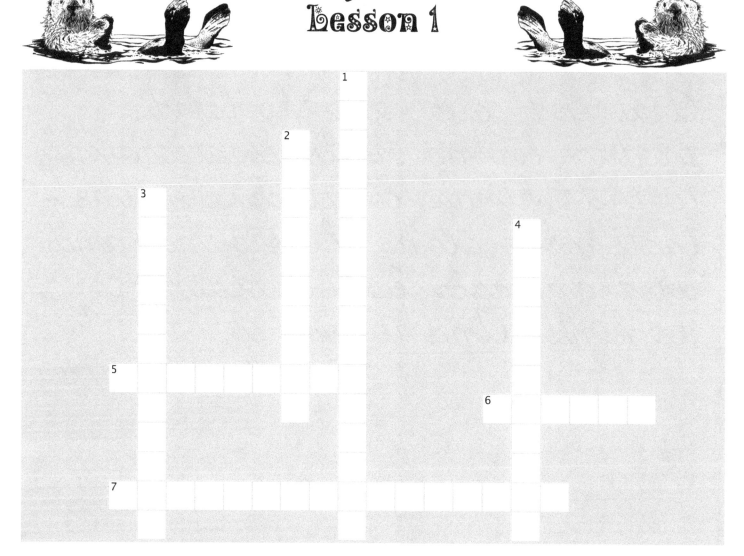

SAFARI   ZOOLOGISTS   HABITUATION   NATURAL SELECTION

UNGULATES   VETERINARIAN   ZOONOTIC DISEASES

Across

5. Animals with hooves.
6. A journey across a stretch of land, usually made to observe or hunt wild animals.
7. The process by which creatures that are best adapted to their environment survive. TWO WORDS

Down

1. Illnesses transmitted between animals and people, like avian flu, mad cow disease, west Nile fever, and Lyme disease. TWO WORDS
2. People who study animal behavior, habitats, anatomy, and everything else they can about animals.
3. A doctor who works with injured and ill animals.
4. The process through which animals get used to people or other things that aren't naturally a part of their surroundings.

ZOOLOGY MINIBOOK
LESSON 1

Paste your Zoology Flap Book
onto this page.

Explore More
Lesson 1
DVD and Book Suggestions

Planet Earth: The Complete BBC Series (2007) presented by Sir David Attenborough for BBC. This visually exquisite natural history series explores eleven geographical regions or habitats and their unique animal citizens, with an emphasis on ecology in response to global warming. Use caution with sensitive viewers as depictions of death are standard.

Life (2010) presented by Sir David Attenborough for BBC. Originally broadcast as part of BBC's Darwin Season, this six-part series exposes the extraordinary behaviors animals have developed in order to survive. Evolutionary content.

Nature: Born Wild (2009) distributed by PBS. An exciting series that gives viewers a rare look at the very first days of a marmoset, a moose, an elephant and a gorilla.

Nature's Most Amazing Events (2009) presented by Sir David Attenborough for BBC. This visually and emotionally dramatic series connects six global climatic phenomena that altered landscapes and habitats to its animal winners and losers.

Walt Disney's Legacy Collection: True Life Adventures, Volumes 1-4. Digitally re-mastered and re-released classics from the 1950's include titles such as African Lion, Jungle Cat, Bear Country, White Wilderness, and so many more!

The Animal Kinds (2009) by Answers in Genesis (ages 5-11). Buddy Davis explores God's design for animals—the camel, dog and horse—during a visit to the Creation Museum's petting zoo.

Life's Story (2004) by Answers in Genesis (ages 8+). This visually stunning wildlife production tackles the hard questions of the theory of evolution, using nature to expose the impossibility of it.

Incredible Creatures That Defy Evolution, Volumes 1-3 (ages 12+). This series explores the intriguing animal designs that cannot be explained by the theory of evolution, pointing instead to a Creator.

Handbook of Nature Study by Anna Comstock (all ages). This classic natural history textbook examines an extensive list of animals, plants and more, with an emphasis on observation.

If Animals Could Talk by William L. Coleman (all ages). Descriptions of the catbird, panda, leopard, and other wonders of nature demonstrate spiritual truths and the importance of living according to the Christian faith.

James Herriot's Treasury for Children by James Herriot (all ages). A collection of delightful tales from a beloved veterinarian and author.

Animalia by Graeme Base (ages 4-8). A visual feast for the eyes, this puzzle book is filled with intricate and detailed illustrations of animals.

The Animals of Maple Hill Farm by Alice and Martin Provensen (ages 4-8). Introduces the animals on the authors' own farm in New York: dogs, horses, pigs, geese, chickens, cows, goats, sheep, cats, and more!

Arnosky's Ark by Jim Arnosky (ages 4-8). Depicts twelve endangered or seriously threatened animals in their natural habitats, emphasizing environmental ecology.

The Big Snow by Berta and Elmer Hader (ages 4-8) Caldecott Medal Winner. In this treasured picture book, woodland animals prepare for winter.

Big Tracks, Little Tracks by Millicent Selsam (ages 4-8). Answers questions about animal habits by examining their respective tracks and other clues left behind. Includes plenty of hands-on activities.

Crinkleroot's Guide to Knowing Animal Habitats by Jim Arnosky (ages 4-8). A picture book that investigates, with a mixture of humor and instruction, the different habitats and their animal residents.

Crinkleroot's Guide to Walking in Wild Places by Jim Arnosky (ages 4-8). Explore nature while taking a walk with Crinkleroot along a woodland trail.

First Encyclopedia of Animals by Usborne Books (ages 4-8). Using simple text combined with extraordinary photography and illustrations, this book offers young readers a fascinating introductory peek into the animal world.

How Animals Talk by Susan McGrath (ages 4-8). Describes how animals communicate with each other by means of sight, sound, smell, and touch.

Keep Looking! by Joyce Hunt and Millicent Selsam (ages 4-8). A colorful picture book that encourages children to look for signs of wild animals in a country landscape by adding a new one to each successive page.

Listen to the Animals: Devotions for Families with Young Children by William L. Coleman (ages 4-8). Fifty-two tales of animals give moral lessons in living according to the Christian faith.

What Color is Camouflage? by Caroline B. Otto (ages 4-8). Explains how the use of camouflage helps both predator and prey.

Who Eats What? Food Chains and Food Webs by Patricia Lauber (ages 4-8). A picture book that illustrates the food chains of land and water animals.

*Be aware that some titles may contain evolutionary content   20

The Year at Maple Hill Farm by Alice and Martin Provensen (ages 4-8). Describes the changes caused by the seasons of a year on a farm and its surrounding countryside.

Animals and Their Young by Pamela Hickman (ages 6-9). Realistic illustrations and clear text examine and compare how different animals reproduce.

Benny's Animals, And How He Put Them in Order by Millicent Selsam (ages 6-9). Two boys, with the help of a professor, learn to divide their animal pictures into proper groups.

Biggest, Strongest, Fastest by Steve Jenkins (ages 6-9). A beautiful picture book about the animal leaders of the world.

Field Trips: Bug Hunting, Animal Tracking, Bird-watching, Shore Walking by Jim Arnosky (ages 6-9). For budding naturalists, a how-to guide for taking nature hikes and keeping journals, emphasizing identification, observation, respect and safety.

Food Chain Frenzy: A Magic School Bus Chapter Book by Anne Capeci (ages 6-9). Take a food chain field trip with the Magic School Bus.

Hidden Animals by Millicent Selsam (ages 6-9). Explains how the ability of certain animals to blend in with or take on the characteristics of their environment protects them from enemies.

How Many Ways Can You Catch a Fly? by Steve Jenkins (ages 6-9). An engaging picture book that explores the different ways animals within the food chain solve similar problems, like escaping predators and catching prey.

Incredible Animal Adventures by Jean Craighead George (ages 6-9). A beloved and famous collection of stories about animals, including Balto, the sled dog that found its way through a blinding snowstorm, and Koko, the gorilla that learned sign language.

Never Smile at a Monkey: And 17 Other Important Things to Remember by Steve Jenkins (ages 6-9). A fascinating picture book explores the unique and often deadly ways wild animals protect themselves or catch prey. Use caution with sensitive children.

Pets in a Jar: Collecting and Keeping Small Wild Animals by Seymour Simon (ages 6-9). A how-to guide for collecting and keeping a number of creatures, using inexpensive and common equipment.

What Do You Do When Something Wants to Eat You? by Steve Jenkins (ages 6-9). Boldly yet simply illustrated, this book introduces to children the defense mechanisms of fourteen different wild animals, showing how they escape their predators.

What Do You Do with a Tail Like This? by Steve Jenkins and Robin Page (ages 6-9) Caldecott Honor Book. Explores peculiar facts about the special uses of animal body parts, like eyes, ears, nose, mouth, and feet.

Watching Desert Life by Jim Arnosky (ages 6-9). With realistic illustrations and engaging narrative, Arnosky takes his readers on a trip to the desert to meet its residents.

Wilderness Ways by William J. Long (ages 8-11). A naturalist shares his keen observations of animals in their natural habitats.

Animals by Janice VanCleave (ages 9-12). A book of simple experiments that helps children answer questions about the habits of animals; also explains how to transform the experiments into science fair projects.

Animals and Their World by Sally Morgan (ages 9-12). Examines how animals are adapted to survive in their respective environments through use of their unique senses and abilities to communicate. Contains numerous experiments that can be done at home or at a nearby park.

One Day in the Desert by Jean Craighead George (ages 9-12). Explains how the animal and human inhabitants of the Sonoran Desert of Arizona—a mountain lion, a roadrunner, a coyote, a tortoise, and members of the Papago Indian tribe—survive its merciless heat.

One Day in the Prairie by Jean Craighead George (ages 9-12). A day in the lives of three animals—the bison, prairie dog and eagle—living on a prairie wildlife refuge as they sense and prepare for a coming tornado.

One Day in the Tropical Rain Forest by Jean Craighead George (ages 9-12). A young native boy helps scientists search for and find a nameless butterfly along the Orinoco River in Venezuela, saving the rain forest from bulldozing.

One Day in the Woods by Jean Craighead George (ages 9-12). A young girl spends the day in the woods and encounters its flora and fauna.

School of the Woods by William J. Long (ages 9-12). Vivid depictions examine how mother animals prepare their young for life in the wild.

Secrets of a Wildlife Watcher by Jim Arnosky (ages 9-12). The author shares techniques used for finding wild animals such as owls, turtles, squirrels, foxes, beavers, and deer, and getting close enough to study their behavior.

Secrets of the Woods by William J. Long (ages 9-12). The author shares his observations of wild animals in their North American habitats.

The View from the Oak by Judith and Herbert R. Kohl (ages 9-12) National Book Award Winner. Encourages readers to view the world of ticks, flies, birds, jelly fish, and other animals through their senses, not our own.

World of Animals by Usborne Books (ages 9-12). Arranged by continent, this Internet-linked book uses stunning photography and informative text to introduce and examine a bevy of animals.

The Burgess Animal Book for Children by Thornton Burgess (ages 6-9). Old Mother Nature introduces elementary children to the mammals of North America.

Tommy Smith's Animals by Edmund Selous (ages 6-9). The story of how one boy became a friend to all the animals of his neighborhood, after meeting them and learning about their habits.

My Zoology Project

Lesson 1

What I did:

What I did:

What I learned:

What I learned:

Scientific Speculation Sheet

Camouflage Experiment

Lesson 1

Name_____   Date _____

Materials Used:

Procedure:

Hypothesis:

Results:

Conclusion:

	Red candies	Brown candies	Green candies	Yellow candies	Orange candies	Blue candies
Starting Number						
Number Found						
Number Not Found						

FASCINATING FACTS

ABOUT

CARNIVOROUS ANIMALS

Lesson 2

ca

FASCINATING FACTS

ABOUT

CARNIVOROUS ANIMALS

Lesson 2

carNivorous
aNimals are
animals that
only eat meat
from otters to
lions all are car

Nivorous

25

What Do You Remember?
Lesson 2 Review Questions

1. What characteristics do mammals have?

2. How can you tell the skull of a mammal from the skull of a reptile?

3. Which sense does a dog use the most?

4. What are some of the ways dogs communicate?

5. What four major kinds of teeth do mammals have?

6. How many of each gene do you have?

7. Where did you get them?

8. If a gene is recessive, what does that mean?

9. How does a pack of dogs usually hunt prey?

10. What do we call the male leader of a pack?

11. What do we call the female leader?

12. Why are wolves so rare today?

13. What is a digitigrade?

"Yes, Lord," she said, "but even the dogs eat the crumbs that fall from their masters' table."

Matthew 15:27

"Yes, Lord," she said, "but even the dogs eat the crumbs that fall from their masters' table."
Matthew 15:27

Vocabulary Crossword
Lesson 2

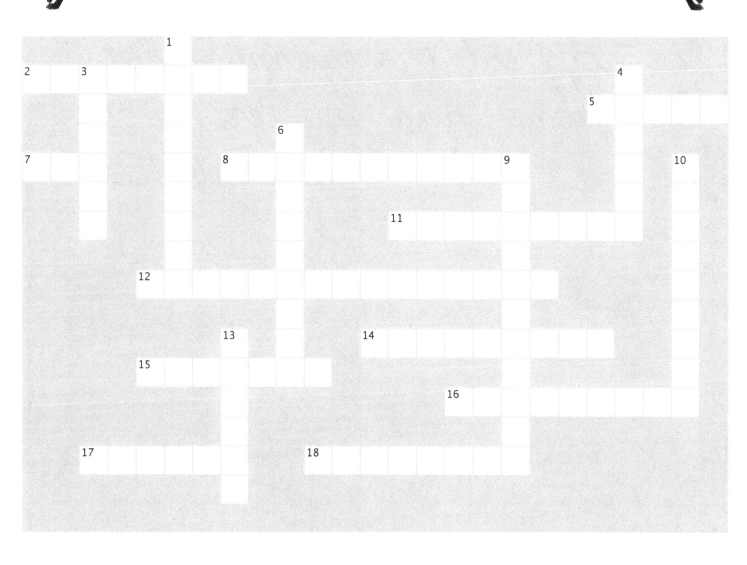

DIGEST

PREMOLARS

DERMIS

SCENT GLANDS

CANIFORMS

DNA

INCISORS

MOLARS

GLANDS

CARNASSIAL TEETH

FELIFORMS

DOMINANT

CANINES

EPIDERMIS

SWEAT GLANDS

CARNIVORA

GENES

RECESSIVE

Vocabulary Crossword
Lesson 2

Across

2. This type of gene will win; its information will be used.
5. The form in which DNA stores information.
7. A molecule that exists in every living creature and stores information that helps the creature be what it is supposed to be.
8. Glands that produce and release a water-based mixture we call sweat. TWO WORDS
11. The outer layer of skin that has hair on it.
12. A carnivore's molars and premolars that are specially designed to cut meat. TWO WORDS
14. Mammals' teeth used for grinding, right behind the canine teeth.
15. Mammals' teeth used for tearing and gripping.
16. A group in order Carnivora that contains dog-like animals.
17. Organs in the body that make and release chemicals.
18. Mammals' teeth used for cutting.

Down

1. An order in the animal kingdom that contains many of the ferocious predators.
3. Mammals' teeth (in the very back of the mouth) used for grinding.
4. The layer of skin under the epidermis; it gets bruised and bleeds.
6. This gene will not be used when the dominant gene is present.
9. Glands that release odors. TWO WORDS
10. A group in order Carnivora that contains cat-like animals.
13. To break down food so it can be turned into energy.

Vocabulary Crossword
Lesson 2

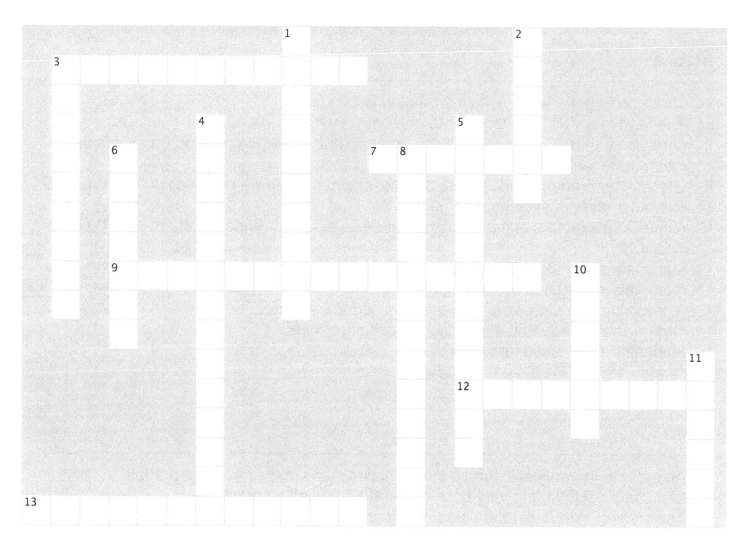

ALPHA MALE
DIGITIGRADES
COYOTES
ARCTIC FOX
RACCOON DOG

DOMINANT PAIR
OLFACTORY ORGANS
RED FOX
JACKAL
AFRICAN WILD DOG

ALPHA FEMALE
WOLVES
OPPORTUNISTIC
DINGOES

Vocabulary Crossword
Lesson 2

Across

3. The female leader in a group of animals. TWO WORDS
7. A species of wolf that is thriving. They are night hunters and are often alone.
9. Organs of smell. TWO WORDS
12. The male leader in a group of animals. TWO WORDS
13. Animals that walk on their toes, giving them the ability to run swiftly.

Down

1. Living only in Japan, this dog looks like a large raccoon. TWO WORDS
2. A type of canine. They have been pests for livestock farmers and a source of fear for travelers at night.
3. A fox that lives in the arctic regions of Europe, Asia, North America, Greenland and Iceland. TWO WORDS
4. A canine that is very social and is often called the "painted wolf." THREE WORDS
5. The two leaders (female and male) in a group of animals. TWO WORDS
6. Australian canines that were once pet dogs owned by Indonesian traders who fished in the waters of Australia thousands of years ago.
8. When an animal changes its diet to fit changes in its surroundings we call it an _____ feeder.
10. An opportunistic omnivore that can live in cities. It looks like a small wolf with really big ears.
11. An opportunistic canine that can eat anything, although it prefers small animals. TWO WORDS

Carnivorous Animals Minibook

Lesson 2

Paste your Carnivorous Animals
Matchbook onto this page.

Explore More

Lesson 2
Science Fair Fun

Develop a science fair project based on some questions you might have about dogs. Below are some examples:

- Are crossbred dogs healthier than purebred dogs?
- Are crossbred dogs smarter or do they learn faster than purebred dogs?
- Do dogs hear music?
- Does your dog see yellow (or another particular color)?
- Do dogs see in black and white or color?
- Decide what you believe and formulate some ideas for testing your belief.

Here's a good resource to help you create a science fair project step by step: *Strategies for Winning Science Fair Projects* by Joyce Henderson and Heather Tomasello.

DVD and Book Suggestions

Lassie Come Home (1943) distributed by MGM. An adaptation of the classic novel written by Eric Knight.

Nature: Dogs (1997) Narrated by John Ritter for PBS. Examines the ties that bind pet owners to their canine companions.

Nature: Man's Best Friend (1987) distributed by PBS. Explores how the dog has moved from pack animal to companion.

Nature: Wolves: In the Valley of the Wolves/Christmas in Yellowstone (2005) distributed by PBS. Two episodes bring viewers face-to-face with a struggling wolf pack and shed light on the habits of foxes, elk, bears and park visitors during the height of the Christmas season.

Old Yeller (1957) distributed by Walt Disney. An adaptation of the classic novel written by Fred Gipson.

Savage Sam (1963) distributed by Disney (sequel to Old Yeller). An adaptation of the classic novel written by Fred Gipson.

Sounder (1972) distributed by Disney; received (4) Academy Award Nominations. An adaptation of the Newberry Medal winning novel written by William H. Armstrong.

Where the Red Fern Grows (1972) distributed by Disney. An adaptation of the classic novel written by Wilson Rawls.

How to Talk to Your Dog by Jean Craighead George (ages 3-6). A brightly colored picture book describes how dogs communicate with sounds and behaviors and how humans can talk back to them.

Nutik, the Wolf Pup by Jean Craighead George (ages 4-8). A brightly illustrated picture book narrates what happens when Amaroq cares for a young wolf pup and grows to love it, although it cannot stay with him.

Nutik and Amaroq Play Ball by Jean Craighead George (ages 4-8). While searching for a missing football, a young Eskimo boy and his wolf pup nearly get lost in the tundra.

Look to the North: A Wolf Pup Diary by Jean Craighead George (ages 4-8). Realistic paintings illustrate the growth of a pack of three wolf pups in the Alaskan tundra.

Wolves by Gail Gibbons (age 4-8). A colorful picture book about the life of a gray wolf that explores its appearance, habitat, diet, and more!

The Wolves Are Back by Jean Craighead George (ages 4-8). A colorful picture book tells how wolves have returned from near-extinction in North America.

Freckles: The Mystery of the Little White Dog in the Desert, a True Story by Paul Howey (ages 6-9). An abandoned dog rescued from the desert becomes a therapy dog working with homeless, abused and otherwise at-risk children.

The Moon of the Fox Pups by Jean Craighead George (ages 6-9). Follows the adventures of five fox pups as they encounter their habitat and its residents in the Cumberland Valley of Pennsylvania.

The Moon of the Gray Wolves by Jean Craighead George (ages 6-9). Follows the adventures of a young wolf pack as they encounter their habitat and its residents in the Tokat Pass of Alaska.

Wild, Wild Wolves by Joyce Milton (ages 6-9). An easy reader introduces children to the pack structure and habits of wolves.

Wolves by Seymour Simon (ages 6-9). Addresses some of the myths and legends about wolves while examining the relationship between wolves and man.

*Be aware that some titles may contain evolutionary content   35

Explore More
Lesson 2
Older Elementary Books Concerning Canines

Bristle Face by Zachary Ball (ages 9-12). A young boy runs away from the home of his brutal uncle and finds a best friend in a funny-looking yet loving dog.

Deadly Game at Stony Creek by Peter Zachary Cohen (ages 9-12). Two teenage boys hunt down a pack of killer, wild dogs.

Desert Dog by Jim Kjelgaard (ages 9-12). After his master dies, a champion greyhound chooses the freedom of the desert where its ready intellect is continually challenged in the battle against thirst, hunger, and natural enemies. May contain anthropomorphism.

Haunt Fox by Jim Kjelgaard (ages 9-12). Star the fox, legendary for always giving hunters the slip, is hunted for a summer and a winter by young Jack and his dog, Thunder.

Lad, A Dog by Albert Payson Terhune (ages 9-12). Originally a collection of popular magazine articles, this book depicts the repeated courage and loyalty of Lad, an extraordinary collie.

Lassie Come Home by Eric Knight (ages 9-12). The American classic tale of one dog's love for and loyalty to its owner, a boy named Joe.

The Midnight Fox by Betsy Byars (ages 9-12). The story of Tom, a ten-year-old boy who is forced to spend his summer on his aunt's farm while his parents vacation in Europe, and his struggle to protect a black fox and her cub.

Rescue Dog of the High Pass by Jim Kjelgaard (ages 9-12). A boy who cannot master book learning but knows the mountains well is accepted as a lay worker at the hospice in St. Bernard Pass, where he and his great mastiff work to prove their worth.

Shiloh by Phyllis Reynolds Naylor (ages 9-12) Newberry Medal Winner. Saving a mistreated beagle pup from an abusive owner isn't as clear-cut as Marty first thought.

Snow Dog by Jim Kjelgaard (ages 9-12). The adventures of a husky dog born in the wilderness and left to fend for itself when a black wolf kills its mother and brothers.

Stormy by Jim Kjelgaard (ages 9.-12). After his father is jailed, a young boy finds himself on his own in the wilderness until he meets a mistreated outlaw dog and works hard to win its affection.

Vulpes, the Red Fox by Jean Craighead George (ages 9-12). The story of a young fox growing up in Maryland that struggles to outwit and outrun his enemies.

Wild Trek by Jim Kjelgaard (ages 9-12). A trapper and his dog travel into the rugged wilderness of northern Canada to rescue a naturalist and a pilot whose plane has been downed.

The Wolfling: A Documentary Novel of the Eighteen-Seventies by Sterling North (ages 9-12). The story of Robbie and his struggle to convince his parents and wolf-hating neighbors that his beloved pet, Wolf—half wolf, half dog—is as hard-working as any dog.

Old Yeller by Fred Gipson (ages 10-14) Newberry Honor Book. The classic tale of how one stray dog through its courage and heart changed the life of a young boy.

Savage Sam by Fred Gipson (ages 10-14). A fast-paced, action-packed sequel to Old Yeller, Savage Sam helps to save a group of kidnapped children and battles wolves and bobcats to defend its masters.

Sounder by William H. Armstrong (ages 10-14) Newberry Medal Winner. The harrowing tale about the son of a jailed, black share-cropper, living in Depression-era Louisiana, and his hunting dog, Sounder.

Along Came a Dog by Meinert De Jong (ages 9-12) Newberry Honor Book. A stray dog earns a home for itself by protecting a little red hen and its chicks from a preying hawk.

The Call of the Wild by Jack London (ages 10-14). The classic tale of the terrific struggle for survival for one man and Buck, his previously domesticated dog, in the frozen Alaskan tundra during the Klondike Gold Rush.

White Fang by Jack London (ages 10-14). Written mostly from the viewpoint of its main character, White Fang details one wild canine's brutal journey to domestication.

My Carnivorous Animals Project
Lesson 2

What I did:

What I did:

What I learned:

What I learned:

Scientific Speculation Sheet

Sight or Smell
Lesson 2

Name_____   Date _____

Materials Used:

Procedure:

Hypothesis:

Results:

Conclusion:

FASCINATING FACTS
ABOUT
CANIFORMS
LESSON 3

Have you ever seen
a bear maybe you
saw a Grizzly bear
or a American black
bear you probably
think they eat meat
while you will be
correct they eat
more food like

fuits, roots, shoots, and
nuts they are caniforms
when winter comes some
people think that the bears
hibernate this false they
go for a long nap while

thinking
you may be thats the
same thing when bears
hibernate they can wake
easly when a animal is
hibernateing they can't
wake 39 easly

What Do You Remember?
Lesson 3 Review Questions

1. What is a plantigrade?

2. Do bears eat mostly meat?

3. What do bears do instead of hibernating?

4. Should you ever feed a bear?

5. Name one way to tell the difference between a black bear and a brown bear.

6. What color is polar bear skin?

7. What is different about a panda's wrist compared with a brown bear's wrist?

8. What kind of otter spends almost all its time in the water?

9. Which is more likely to have rabies, a skunk or a raccoon?

BEARS

SKUNKS

_____
_____
_____
_____
_____

PROKYONIDS

_____
_____
_____
_____
_____

MUSTELIDS

_____
_____
_____
_____
_____

IF YOU SEE A BEAR
LESSON 3

DON'T RUN	DON'T CLIMB
FACE THE BEAR	DON'T MAKE EYE CONTACT
BACK AWAY	WAVE YOUR ARMS & YELL
FIGHT BACK	HUDDLE UP WITH OTHERS

When a lion or a bear came and carried off a sheep from the flock. I went after it, struck it and rescued the sheep from its mouth.

1 Samuel 17:34-35

When a lion or a bear came
and carried off a sheep from
the flock, I went after it,
struck it and rescued the sheep
from its mouth.

1 Samuel 17:34-35

Vocabulary Crossword
Lesson 3

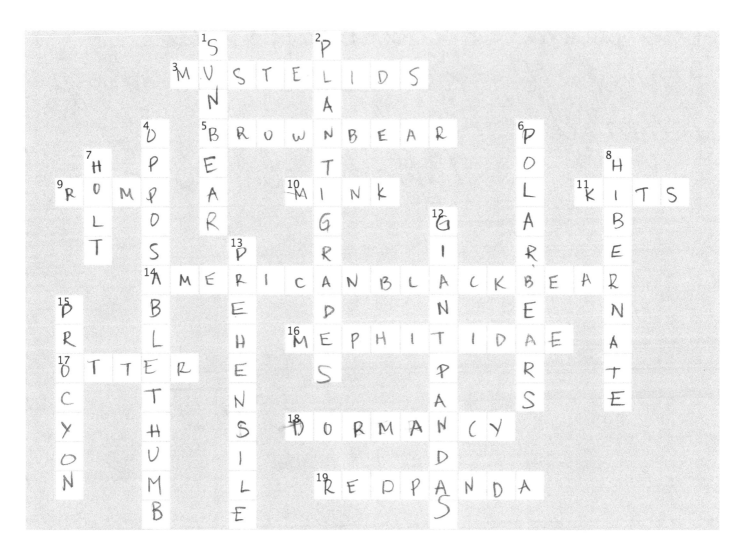

PLANTIGRADES
BROWN BEAR
SUN BEAR
MINK
ROMP
PROCYON
RED PANDA

HIBERNATE
AMERICAN BLACK BEAR
GIANT PANDAS
MUSTELIDS
HOLT
KITS

DORMANCY
POLAR BEARS
OPPOSABLE THUMB
OTTER
MEPHITIDAE
PREHENSILE

Vocabulary Crossword
Lesson 3

Across

3. Members of the family Mustelidae. They have luxuriously soft fur.
5. A type of bear that includes grizzly bears and Kodiak bears. It has a large "muscle hump" above the shoulders. TWO WORDS
9. A group of otters.
10. A small, ferret-like creature with unusually soft fur.
11. Baby raccoons.
14. A species of bear that is the most abundant bear in North America. It was the inspiration for the original teddy bear. THREE WORDS
16. The family in which skunks belong. The name comes from the Latin word mephit, which means "foul odor."
17. A playful creature that is carnivorous and can be found in rivers, streams and oceans all over the world.
18. A state of temporary inactivity, or a long, quiet nap.
19. A member of the Procyonidae family. It can be found in Southeast Asia and has the ringed tail and face markings of a raccoon. TWO WORDS

Down

1. This bear has short, sleek fur and golden markings. It is also called a "dog bear," because it is sometimes kept as a pet. TWO WORDS
2. Animals that walk on the entire bottom of the foot, as opposed to walking on their toes.
4. A thumb that can move around and be placed across the other fingers to help grab things. TWO WORDS
6. These bears live in the Arctic and have whitish-yellow fur. TWO WORDS
7. An otter's home.
8. What an animal does to slow its breathing down a lot and lower its body temperature to a point where it is almost the same temperature as the surrounding air.
12. These adorable black and white bears are native to China. TWO WORDS
13. An unusually long tail that can be used to grasp things is called a _____ tail.
15. Raccoons make up this genus of the family Procyonidae.

CANIFORMS MINIBOOK
LESSON 3

Paste your Bears Tab Book onto
this page.

Explore More
Lesson 3

DVD and Book Suggestions

The Bear (1989) distributed by Sony Pictures. With almost no dialog, this movie provides an up-close look at the habits of bears.

King of the Grizzlies (1970) distributed by Disney. Based on The Biography of a Grizzly by Ernest Thompson Seton.

Nature: Bears (1982) distributed by PBS. Follows these big, furry animals as they awaken from hibernation and hunt for salmon.

Nature: Pandas (1982) Narrated by Matthew Modine for PBS. Travels to both mountainous China and the San Diego Zoo to examine the life of pandas in the wild and captivity, respectively.

Rascal (1969) distributed by Disney. The story of a boy and his rescued pet raccoon.

Ring of Bright Water (1969) distributed by MGM. The adventures of a man and his otter pet, as together they move from the big city of London to the Scottish coast.

Bamboo Valley: A Story of a Chinese Bamboo Forest by Anne Whitehead Nagda (ages 4-8). Colorful illustrations and expressive text follow a young panda as he searches for a range of his own for food and shelter.

Giant Pandas by Gail Gibbons (ages 4-8). Introduces young children to the appearance, habits and life cycle of the Giant Panda.

Otters Under Water by Jim Arnosky (ages 4-8). A delightful picture book that shows two young otters swimming, frolicking and eating at a pond.

A Panda's World by Caroline Arnold (ages 4-8). A boldly illustrated picture book packed with facts about the life cycle and habits of pandas.

A Polar Bear Journey by Debbie S. Miller (ages 4-8). Lovely acrylic paintings and rhyming text depict the interaction between one mother polar bear and her cubs.

Polar Bears by Gail Gibbons (ages 4-8). A gentle introduction to the appearance, habits and life cycle of the Polar Bear.

Welcome to the World of Otters by Diane Swanson (ages 4-8). Introduces children to the world of otters through amazing facts and color photographs.

Welcome to the World of Raccoons by Diane Swanson (ages 4-8). Introduces children to the world of raccoons through amazing facts and color photographs.

Welcome to the World of Skunks by Diane Swanson (ages 4-8). Introduces children to the world of skunks through amazing facts and color photographs.

Bears: Polar Bears, Black Bears, and Grizzly Bears by Deborah Hodge (ages 6-9). Examines the appearance and habits of three North American bears.

The Moon of the Bears by Jean Craighead George (ages 6-9). Follows one year in the life of a Black Bear, beginning with her emerging from hibernation in the Smoky Mountains of Tennessee.

The Bears of Blue River by Charles Major (ages 9-12). While learning the ways of the woods, a pioneer boy grows up in early nineteenth-century Indiana and has many exciting and dangerous encounters with bears.

The Biography of a Grizzly by Ernest Thompson Seton (ages 9-12). The fortunes and misfortunes of a lone grizzly bear that learns early its enemy is man.

Gentle Ben by Walt Morey (ages 9-12). A classic narrative about the remarkable friendship between a grieving boy and an Alaskan brown bear.

Meph, the Pet Skunk by John L. and Jean Craighead George (ages 9-12). A heartwarming tale about a boy who discovers and cares for a young skunk under his farmhouse.

Rascal: A Memoir of a Better Era by Sterling North (ages 9-12) Newberry Honor Book. An exciting yearlong adventure between a boy and his best friend, a young raccoon.

Vison, the Mink by John L. George (ages 9-12). Vividly describes the life or death struggles of a mink living along the Muddy Branch in Maryland.

Where the Red Fern Grows by Wilson Rawls (ages 9-12). Dogs, Raccoons, and Mountain Lions are explored in this unforgettable American classic.

My Bears Project
Lesson 3

What I did:

What I learned:

Scientific Speculation Sheet

Color and Temperature

Lesson 3

Name_____   Date _____

Materials Used:

Procedure:

Hypothesis:

Results:

Conclusion:

FASCINATING FACTS

ABOUT Felíforms

Lesson 4

have you ever seen a wi'ld lion, cheetah, or bobcat all feliforms Have claws tieeth and swift reflexs do you know one of the

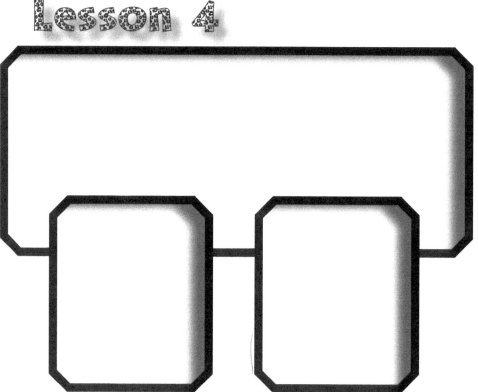

most inporten part of a cat? its the wiskers cat can see objects in the dank becouse of their wiskers they can feel a big log with their wiskers

52

FASCINATING FACTS

ABOUT Feliforms

Lesson 4

FASCINATING FACTS

ABOUT Feliforms

Lesson 4

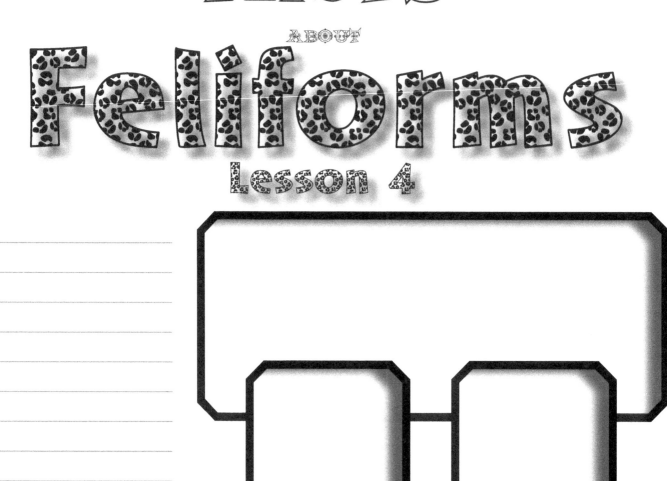

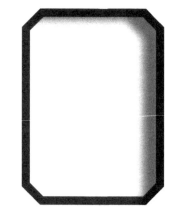

What Do You Remember?
Lesson 4 Review Questions

1. What special sensory organ do cats have?

2. If a leopard or jaguar is black, what is it often called?

3. Which cat cannot retract its claws?

4. What is an apex predator?

5. Which cat forms strong family bonds?

6. Which cat is the most dangerous to humans?

7. Which cat is the fastest runner?

8. Name the three wildcats that live in North America.

9. Which requires the largest hunting territory?

10. How is a hyena similar to a dog?

11. How is it similar to a cat?

12. How is the spotted hyena different from other hyenas?

13. What does an aardwolf eat?

14. What is a mutation?

15. What kind of homes do creatures from the family Herpestidae create for themselves?

16. Which animal is the mongoose famous for being able to kill?

17. How do meerkats care for their family members?

Story

board

Feliform Fact Sheet
Lesson 4

Feliform Fact Sheet
Lesson 4

When he came near the den, he called to Daniel in an anguished voice, "Daniel, servant of the living God, has your God, whom you serve continually, been able to rescue you from the lions?"

Daniel 6:20

When he came near the den, he called to Daniel in an anguished voice, "Daniel, servant of the living God, has your God, whom you serve continually, been able to rescue you from the lions?"

Daniel 6:20

Vocabulary Crossword
Lesson 4

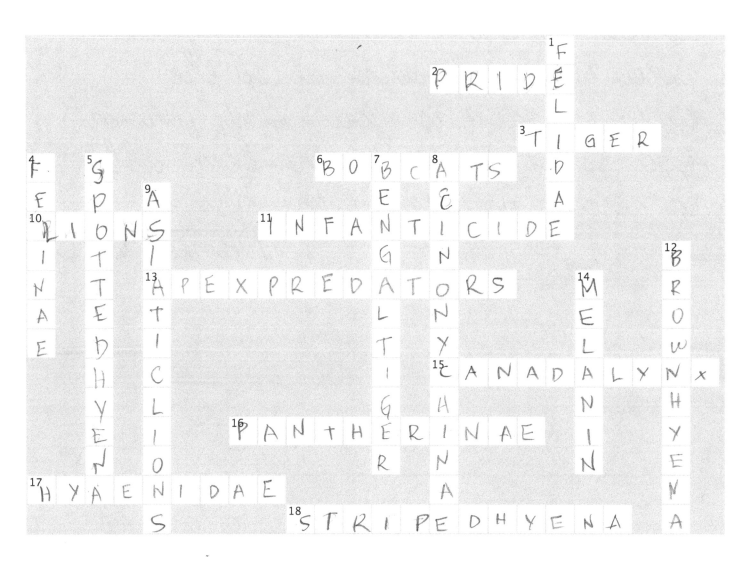

Across

2. PRIDE
3. TIGER
6. BOBCATS
10. LIONS
11. INFANTICIDE
13. APEX PREDATORS
15. CANADA LYNX
16. PANTHERINAE
17. HYAENIDAE
18. STRIPED HYENA

Down

1. FELIDAE
4. FELINAE
5. SPOTTED HYENA
7. BENGAL TIGER
8. ACINONYCHINAE
9. ASIATIC LIONS
12. BROWN HYENA
14. MELANIN

FELIDAE   MELANIN   FELINAE
PANTHERINAE   ACINONYCHINAE   APEX PREDATORS
BENGAL TIGER   LIONS   PRIDE
INFANTICIDE   SPOTTED HYENA   ASIATIC LIONS
TIGER   CANADA LYNX   BOBCATS
HYAENIDAE   BROWN HYENA   STRIPED HYENA

Vocabulary Crossword
Lesson 4

Across

2. A social group of lions. It can have up to 40 or 50 members.
3. A member of subfamily Pantherinae. It is the only animal that can single-handedly attack and bring down a grown Asian elephant.
6. These tan cats have tabby-like streaks of black throughout their spotted coats and look a lot like a house cat.
10. Unlike other cats, these animals form strong, supportive, and caring social groups that stick together and nurture one another.
11. The killing of infants and other very young animals. The new top male in the pride will do this to all cubs sired by the former top male.
13. Animals that are not considered typical prey for other animals. TWO WORDS
15. This wild cat has a short tail, black tufts at the tips of the ears and a double pointed "beard." TWO WORDS
16. The "roaring" cats, like lions, tigers, jaguars and leopards are placed in this subfamily.
17. The name of the feliform family to which hyenas belong.
18. The hyena that is native to northern Africa, the Middle East and Asia. TWO WORDS

Down

1. The family to which all true cats belong.
4. This subfamily contains the "small" cats, like house cats and lynxes.
5. A ferocious animal with the most powerful bite in the animal kingdom. TWO WORDS
7. The cat with the worst reputation for eating man. TWO WORDS
8. This subfamily name comes from two Greek words that mean "thorn" and "claw." The cheetah is placed in this subfamily.
9. Lions that live in India. They are fewer in number than African lions and are smaller in size with shorter manes. TWO WORDS
12. This hyena has shaggy fur and pointed ears. TWO WORDS
14. A chemical that makes skin and fur dark. The black panther's fur is black because of it.

Vocabulary Crossword
Lesson 4

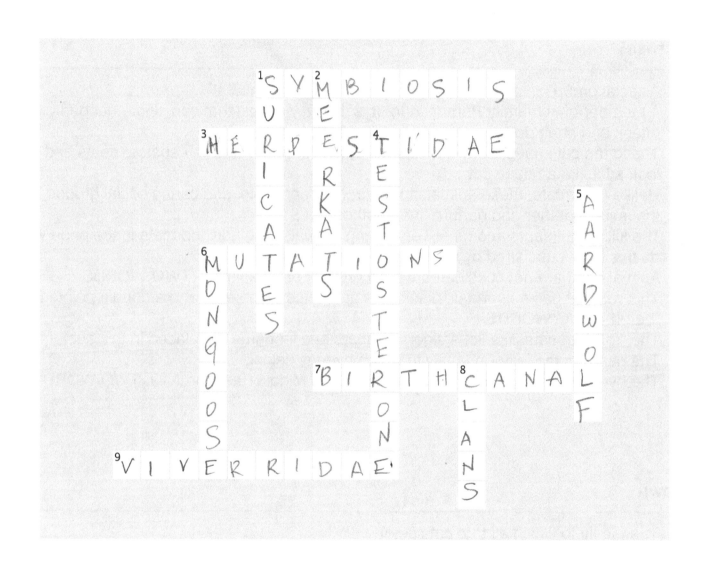

Across / Down grid letters:

¹S Y ²M B I O S I S
U R E
³H E R P E S ⁴T I D A E
R R E
I K S
C A T
A T O S ⁵A
⁶M U T A T I O N S A
O E S R
N S T D
G E W
O R ⁷B I R T H ⁸C A N A L
O O L
S N ⁹V I V E R R I D A E C F
L
A
N
S

AARDWOLF   **CLANS**   **MUTATIONS**
BIRTH CANAL   **TESTOSTERONE**   **VIVERRIDAE**
HERPESTIDAE   **MONGOOSE**   **SYMBIOSIS**
SURICATES   **MEERKATS**

Vocabulary Crossword
Lesson 4

Across

1. A kind of relationship God designed that enables creatures to work and live together so all can benefit.
3. Members of this family live in underground tunnels, eating mostly beetles and other creatures that live in the dirt.
6. Changes to an animal's genes that often cause deformities or diseases. They can be passed on from parent to offspring.
7. The passage that a mammal must pass through when it is being born. TWO WORDS
9. Feliforms that look and act a lot like long-nosed cats belong to this family.

Down

1. Another name for meerkats.
2. Also called suricates, these social creatures live underground in tunnels and are likely to die without their colony.
4. A chemical common in male mammals that causes aggression in hyena cubs.
5. This species of hyena has two populations: one in the southern parts of Africa and one in the northern parts.
6. One of the most dangerous animals in the world. Because of its speed, it is able to avoid most of the quick strikes of a snake.
8. What we call the groups that hyenas form.

Feliforms Minibook
Lesson 4

Paste your Feliforms Layered
Book onto this page.

Born Free (1966) distributed by Columbia Pictures. The true story of how one couple raised an orphaned lioness to adulthood and the challenges of releasing her back into the wilds of Kenya.

Cheetah (1989) distributed by Disney. While living in Kenya with their scientist parents, two teenagers adopt a cheetah only to realize they must return it back to life in the wild.

Charlie, the Lonesome Cougar (1967) distributed by Disney. A forester adopts an abandoned cougar and raises it as a pet until he realizes he must release it back into the wild.

Duma (2005) distributed by Warner Brothers. A young boy adopts an orphaned cheetah cub, raising it on his family's farm, but must return it to the wild after his father's death and his family's subsequent move to the city.

Eye of the Leopard narrated by Jeremy Irons for National Geographic. Follows one mother leopard and her cub as they struggle to survive in their natural habitat.

Meerkat Manor, Seasons 1-4; a television series by Animal Planet. A record of the daily lives of a clan of meerkats named The Whiskers.

Nature: Big Cats (2005) Narrated by Sir David Attenborough for PBS. Footage culled from over fourteen years of filming; includes the elusive and swift jaguar.

Nature: Leopards and Lions (2006) distributed by PBS. Explores the feral world of these two big cats: the snow leopard of the Himalayas and the lion of sub-Saharan Africa.

Chuck Jones' Rikki-Tikki-Tavi by Rudyard Kipling (ages 3-6). A gentle retelling of Kipling's classic in which a mongoose kills a pair of cobras and saves a family.

***How to Talk to Your Cat* by** Jean Craighead George (ages 4-8). This fun picture book mixes photographs of the author with cartoon illustrations of cats as it explains the fascinating ways in which cats communicate.

Meerkat in Trouble by Allan Freewin Jones (ages 4-8). A gentle introduction for young children to a family of Meerkats and the danger they encounter one day.

Rikki-Tikki-Tavi, contained in The Jungle Book by Rudyard Kipling (ages 6+). A gripping adventure about a mongoose that kills a pair of cobras and saves a family.

Akimbo and the Lions by Alexander McCall Smith (ages 6-9). Akimbo and his park ranger father unintentionally capture a lion cub near an African game park.

Hunter in the Snow: The Lynx by Susan Bonners (ages 6-9). A picture book that traces the life cycle of a female Canadian lynx.

The Moon of the Mountain Lions by Jean Craighead George (ages 6-9). Follows one mountain lion on his seasonal migration from the tree line of Mount Olympus to the coast of the Washington Rain Forest.

Wildcats: Cougars, Bobcats, and Lynx by Deborah Hodge (ages 6-9). Soft watercolors and simple text introduce children to the wild cats of North America.

Bobcat: North America's Cat by Stephen R. Swinburne (ages 9-12). A naturalist hunts in Vermont for the elusive bobcat, with the help of a sixth-grade class of students.

The Incredible Journey by Shelia Burnford (ages 9-12). The gripping story of three animal companions—two dogs and one cat—who set out on a perilous journey home through the Canadian wilderness.

The Cats of Roxville Station by Jean Craighead George (ages 9-12). The realistic tale about one abandoned kitten that integrates herself into a feral cat society and Mike, the foster child who loves and longs for her.

Christian the Lion by Anthony Bourke and John Rendall (ages 9-12). How two antique dealers in London raise a lion cub in the city until they realize it must be released back into the wild; there's also a companion movie entitled Christian: The Lion at World's End (1971).

Cougar Threat: Book One in the Danny and Life on Bluff Point Series by Mary Stagnitto (ages 9-12). Ten year-old Danny struggles to be a help to his frontier family on their fruit and livestock farm in 1894.

My Side of the Mountain by Jean Craighead George (age 9-12). The story of a runaway boy who uses his wits to survive in the wild Catskill Mountains of upstate New York, with a weasel and a falcon for companions.

Meerkat Manor: Flower of the Kalahari by Tim Clutton-Brock (ages 10-14). Written by a Cambridge professor, this book provides a detailed and up-close look at a clan of meerkats called the Whiskers.

Saving the Ghost of the Mountain: An Expedition Among Snow Leopards in Mongolia by Sy Montgomery (ages 10-14). An exciting expedition of a crew of scientists hoping to track and sight the elusive snow leopard in the mountains of Mongolia.

*Be aware that some titles may contain evolutionary content

My Feliform Project
Lesson 4

What I did:

What I learned:

Scientific Speculation Sheet

Population Study
Lesson 4

Name_____   Date _____

Materials Used:

Procedure:

Hypothesis:

Results:

Conclusion:

The Cougar Eats the Deer
Lesson 4

Generation	Number of Cougars in Territory	Number of Deer Eaten	Number of Deer That Survived
1.			
2.			
3.			
4.			
5.			
6.			
7.			
8.			
9.			
10.			
11.			
12.			
13.			
14.			
15.			
16.			
17.			
18.			
19.			
20.			

The images of the cougar and deer that you will use for this experiment
are found in the appendix.

FASCINATING FACTS ABOUT Marsupials
Lesson 5

FASCINATING FACTS ABOUT Marsupials

Lesson 5

Cut out this map to use for the Try This! on page 73

One World – The Earth Pieced Together

What Do You Remember?
Lesson 5 Review Questions

1. What do most female marsupials have that other female animals do not?

2. Where do most marsupials live?

3. What was Pangaea?

4. Name some of the animals that are marsupials.

5. What are marsupial young called?

6. What is the difference between a wallaby and a kangaroo?

7. Do animals that are herbivores always stay herbivores?

8. Why is it incorrect to refer to the cute Australian animals as *koala bears*?

9. What do koalas do most of the day?

10. How is the Tasmanian devil like a hyena?

11. How many species of marsupials live in North America?

12. Explain the defense mechanism of the Virginia opossum.

13. How can some marsupial joeys develop without a pouch?

Comparing Possums
Lesson 5

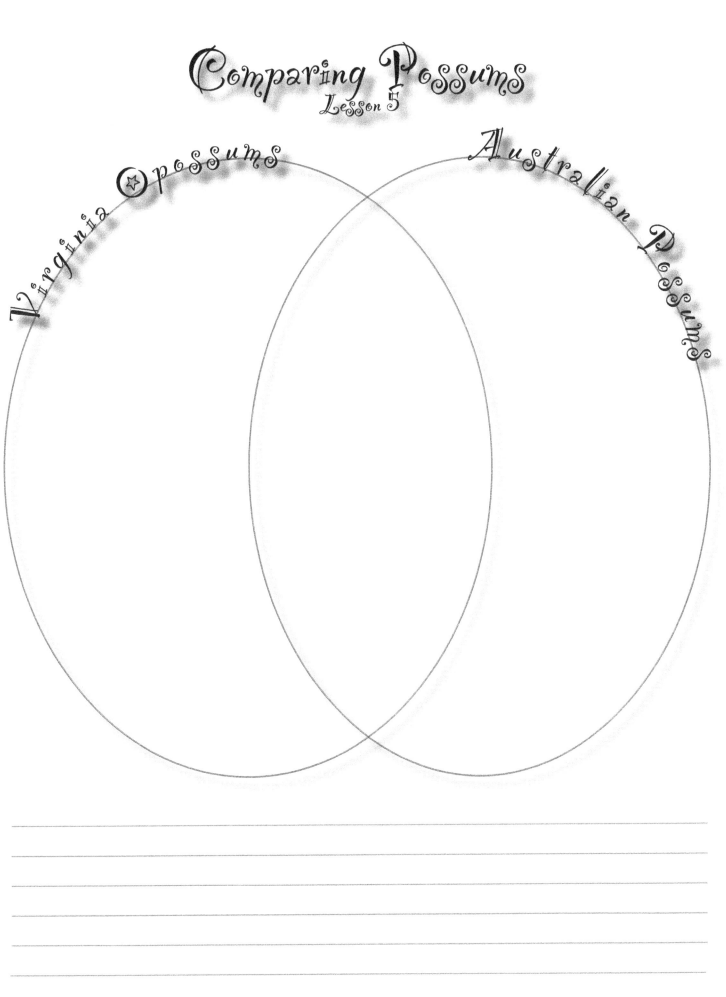

Virginia Opossums

Australian Possums

Australian Marsupials

Lesson 5

Kangaroo/Wallaby

Koala

Wombat

Bettong/Potoroo

Bandicoot/Bilby

Marsupial Mole

Possum

Tasmanian Marsupials

Tasmanian Devil

American Marsupials

Virginia Opossum

South American Opossum

The Sovereign LORD will wipe away the tears from all faces; he will remove the disgrace of his people from all the earth. The LORD has spoken.

Isaiah 25:8

The Sovereign LORD will wipe away the tears from all faces; he will remove the disgrace of his people from all the earth. The LORD has spoken.

Isaiah 25:8

Vocabulary Crossword
Lesson 5

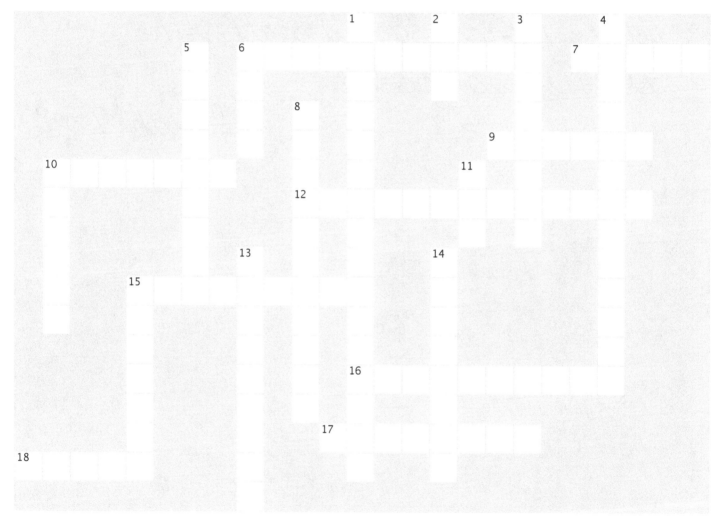

JOEYS	PLACENTAL	MARSUPIUM
PANGAEA	LAND BRIDGES	DIPROTODONTIA
MARSUPIALIA	MACROPOD	DOE
BUCKS	MOBS	WALLABIES
BETTONGS	POTOROOS	KOALAS
WOMBATS	VOMBATIFORMES	ABORIGINES
EUCALYPTUS LEAVES	PAP	POSSUM

Vocabulary Crossword
Lesson 5

Across

6. Many scientists put all marsupials into this single order.
7. Marsupial babies.
9. Animals with round, fuzzy ears. They stay up in trees, rarely coming down to the ground.
10. The big piece of land scientists think split apart to form the continents we have today.
12. All the animals in this order have two front teeth that stick almost straight out from their lower jaw.
15. Animals that look like kangaroos but are smaller in size.
16. The word "koala" comes from the language of these native Australians.
17. Rat-sized macropods that have prehensile tails.
18. A term used to refer to many male animals, including male kangaroos.

Down

1. What the koala eats. TWO WORDS
2. Special milk a mother kangaroo makes.
3. Its name means "big foot." A kangaroo is considered one of these.
4. Wombat-shaped animals.
5. This describes mammals in which the baby develops inside its mother and gets everything it needs from her.
6. Kangaroos form these large groups.
8. Little trails of land that once connected the continents together. TWO WORDS
10. The Australian name given to the mostly tree-dwelling marsupials of the land.
11. A term used to refer to many female animals, including female kangaroos.
13. Joeys develop and find protection inside this special pouch.
14. These "rat kangaroos" are becoming endangered in Australia.
15. These animals have the appearance of extremely furry pigs.

Vocabulary Crossword
Lesson 5

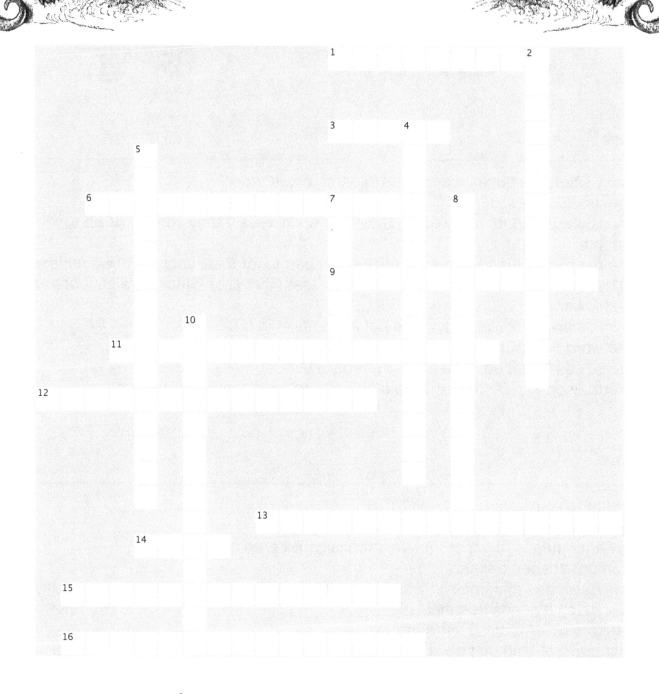

OPOSSUM
BRUSHTAIL POSSUM
BANDICOOT
NOTORYCTEMORPHIA
TASMANIAN DEVIL
MONITO DEL MONTE

VIRGINIA OPOSSUM
RINGTAIL POSSUM
MARSUPIAL MOLES
TASMANIAN TIGER
DIDELPHIMORPHIA

SUGAR GLIDER
PERAMELEMORPHIA
MICROBIOTHERIA
WOMB
BILBY

Vocabulary Crossword
Lesson 5

Across

1. This marsupial looks like a rat and lives alone, building its nest in shallow holes in the ground.
3. A marsupial that looks like a cross between a rat and a rabbit, having a long nose and long ears. It lives in tunnels and is considered endangered.
6. These blind marsupials have fore-claws that look like miniature spades. Their noses are covered with a horny shield that protects them as they push through the dirt. TWO WORDS
9. A species of possum that eats sugar, glides through the air and can be lured to feeding places. TWO WORDS
11. The name for this order comes from Greek words meaning "one who digs in the south."
12. The Monito del Monte is the only living member of this order.
13. Some of the New World marsupials are placed in this order. Its name means "two wombs."
14. The place where an animal or human embryo grows until it is born.
15. This fierce flesh-eater was once common in Australia, but it went extinct in the 1930's. TWO WORDS
16. The order to which the bandicoot and bilby belong.

Down

2. A wombat-looking creature with jet-black fur. The name of its genus means "flesh lover," and it produces terrifying screams when defending its food. TWO WORDS
4. This possum has fur on its tail. TWO WORDS
5. The only North American marsupial. TWO WORDS
7. What the American version of a possum is called.
8. One of the two possums that are considered Australian pests, moving into attics and awakening sleepers with their raucous sounds. TWO WORDS
10. Its name means "little mountain monkey," and it lives in the mountains of Chile and Argentina. THREE WORDS

Marsupials Minibook
Lesson 5

Paste your Marsupials Flap Book
onto this page.

Lesson 5

Make a Marsupial Pouch

Whether it's an opossum, kangaroo or koala, all marsupial babies are called joeys. The mamas' pouches are different though. A kangaroo's is much like a zippered bag with the pouch opening at the top. The koala's pouch opens on the bottom, and the opossum's pouch is more like a flap of skin. Let's make a marsupial pouch!

You will need:
A sheet of cardstock
A sheet of construction paper
Glue
A zippered plastic bag for a kangaroo or koala pouch
Fake fur

First decide which marsupial pouch you want to make. For a kangaroo, glue the bag to the cardstock with the opening at the top. For a koala, glue it with the opening on the bottom. And for an opossum, just glue a rectangle of construction paper on three sides so it makes a pouch. Now, glue fur to the bag or paper flap, making sure to cover the front and sides. If you have enough fur, you can cover the rest of the cardstock to make the pouch blend in. Make sure your joey can get into the pouch!

Next make several joeys of different sizes from your construction paper. Newborn joeys are about the size of a jelly bean. Once they make the journey to the pouch, they stay there until they are big enough to explore. That's about 6 months for koalas and opossums and up to 9 months for a kangaroo. When they are big enough to come out, they will continue to drink milk from their moms, and the koala and opossum will ride on moms' backs. Kangaroo joeys, however, will keep riding around in the pouch until they are too big to fit!

Explore More
Lesson 5

DVD and Book Suggestions

Grainger's World: Yindi, the Last Koala? (2008) Distributed by Goldhil Home Media. Recorded over a period of one year along eastern Australia, a young koala is raised by man after its mother is injured in a car accident.

Animals Do the Strangest Things by Leonora Hornblow (ages 4-8). Describes nineteen animals that have peculiar and strange characteristics, including the platypus that has poison spurs on its legs, the opossum that fools its enemies by pretending to be dead, and the bat that navigates by built-in sonar.

Diary of a Wombat by Jackie French (age 4-8). A whimsical picture book containing a character study of one wombat that spends a week with a human family.

There's an Opossum in My Backyard by Gay Bogue (ages 4-8). A picture book that provides an up-close look at an opossum.

Finding Home by Sandra Markle (ages 6-9). Based on a true story, a mother koala and her joey survive a bush fire and search for food and a new home.

Koala Country: A Story of an Australian Eucalyptus Forest by Deborah Dennard (ages 6-9). A picture book that introduces young readers to the flora and fauna of the koala's habitat.

A Koala's World by Carolina Arnold (ages 6-9). A boldly illustrated picture book packed with facts about the life and habits of koalas.

A Wombat's World by Caroline Arnold (ages 6-9). A boldly illustrated picture book packed with facts about the life and habits of wombats.

Young Kangaroo by Margaret Wise Brown (ages 6-9). A picture book depicting the journey of one young kangaroo as he moves from birth to pouch to the world around him.

How to Scratch a Wombat: Where to Find It . . . What to Feed It . . . Why It Sleeps All Day by Jackie French (ages 9-12). Details the physical characteristics and habits of wombats, with instructions for tracking and observing them yourself.

Pocket Babies and Other Amazing Marsupials by Sneed B. Collard (ages 9-12). Enhanced with color photographs, this book provides a more detailed introduction to the world of marsupials.

Possum by Robert McClung (ages 9-12). A baby opossum grows old enough to leave its mother, surviving the dangers of finding a den and having its own babies.

The Quest for the Tree Kangaroo: An Expedition to the Cloud Forest of New Guinea by Sy Montgomery (ages 9-12). A naturalist documents his participation in an expedition to the forests of Papua New Guinea in search of the elusive and fascinating Matschie's tree kangaroo.

Tasmanian Devil: On Location by Kathy Darling (ages 9-12). A detailed look at the life cycle and habits of the vicious Tasmanian Devil through color photography and informative text.

Wallaby Creek by Joyce Ann Powzyk (ages 9-12). Through lovely watercolors and gentle text, the author shares her observations of the animals she encountered during her stay at Wallaby Creek in Australia.

*Be aware that some titles may contain evolutionary content

My Marsupial Projects
Lesson 5

What I did:

What I did:

What I learned:

What I learned:

FASCINATING FACTS ABOUT PRIMATES

LESSON 6

have you been to the zoo? if you have gone to the zoo you mitgh have seen a primat, a Primat is monkeys, and gorilla's

FASCINATING FACTS

ABOUT

PRIMATES

LESSON 6

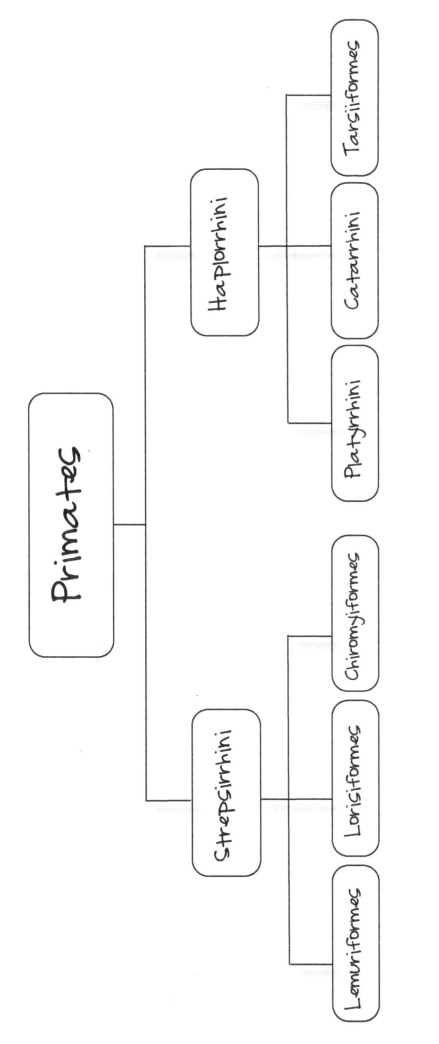

What Do You Remember?
Lesson 6 Review Questions

1. How are primates different from people?

2. Explain how primates are similar to other wild animals.

3. Are most primates social or solitary?

4. What single feature is used to classify the major groups of primates?

5. Name a New World monkey.

6. Name an Old World monkey.

7. What is the difference between monkeys and apes?

8. Which animal is considered a lesser ape?

9. Tell someone a little bit about some of the animals you have studied in this lesson.

EXPLORE.

LEARN ABOUT.

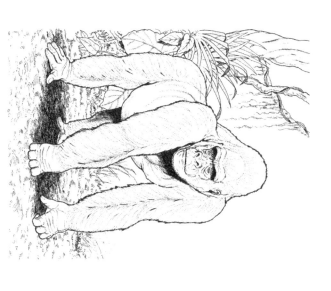

MEET.

COME
EXPLORE
AFRICA

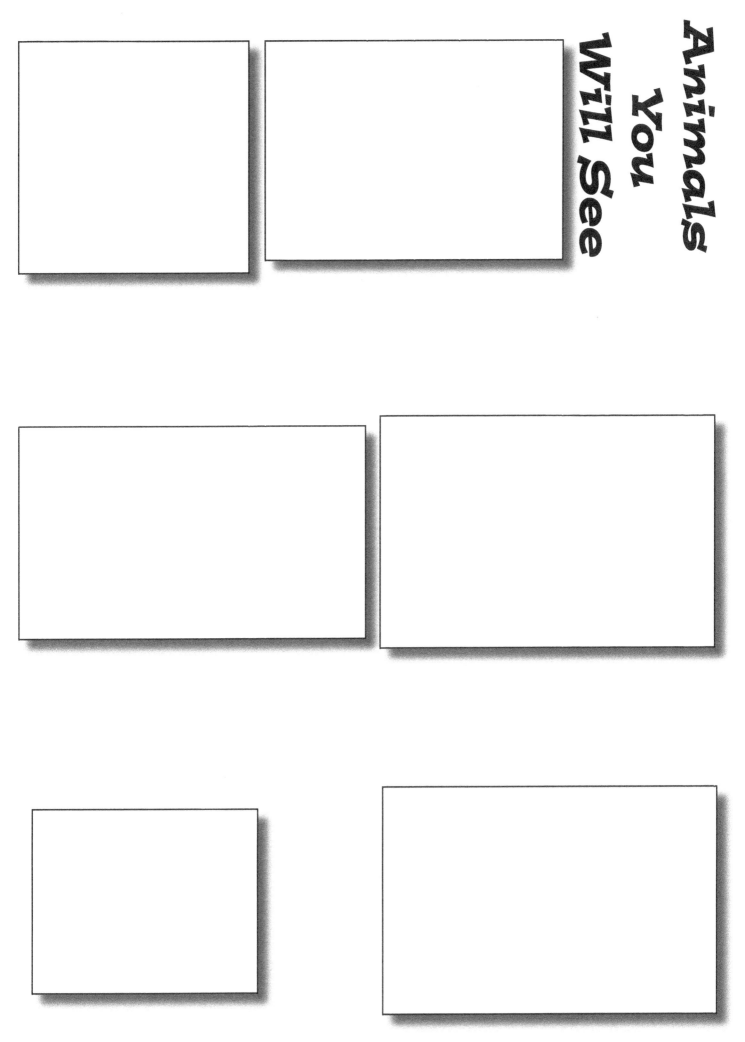

Animals You Will See

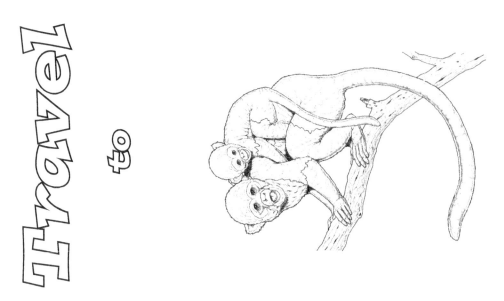

Travel to

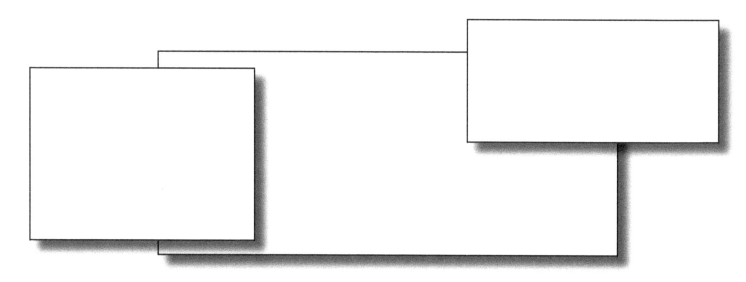

Make a pocket by gluing the bottom and two sides of a piece of paper onto this page, leaving the top side open.

Place your brochures inside your pocket!

Then the LORD God formed man of dust from the ground, and breathed into his nostrils the breath of life; and man became a living being.

Genesis 2:7

Then the LORD God formed man of dust from the ground, and breathed into his nostrils the breath of life; and man became a living being.

Genesis 2:7

Vocabulary Crossword
Lesson 6

PRIMATES
HAPLORRHINI
NEW WORLD MONKEYS
TAMARIN
CERCOPITHECINAE

BINOCULAR VISION
TARSIER
ARBOREAL
COLOBINAE

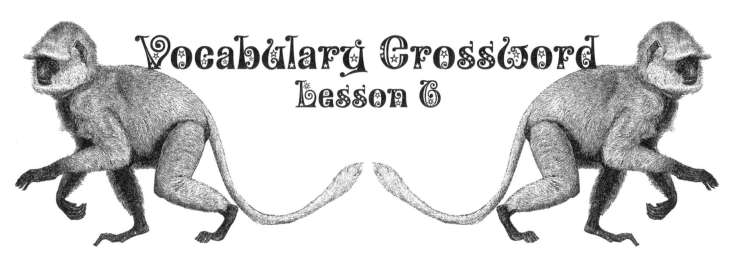

Vocabulary Crossword
Lesson 6

Across

4. This suborder contains the primates you are most likely to see in the zoo.
5. A type of vision that allows animals to judge depth, perceiving how far away things are. TWO WORDS
6. In this type of New World monkey, the father does most of the carrying of the young, bringing it to the mother only to nurse.
7. The primates in this group are mostly herbivorous, live in trees and don't have pouches in their cheeks to store food.
8. Monkeys that are found only in the New World. THREE WORDS

Down

1. The primates in this group are omnivorous and have pouches in their cheeks to store food.
2. Clever creatures with forward-facing eyes. They live in the jungles and most hang high up in the trees.
3. A term that describes animals that live and spend most of their time in trees.
6. This animal gets its name from its extremely long tarsus (ankle) bone. It is the smallest primate in the world.

Vocabulary Crossword
Lesson 6

1

2

3

4   5

6   7

8

9

10   11

12

13

14
15

PROBOSCIS MONKEY
MANDRILLS
DRILL
GIBBONS
BONOBOS

JAPANESE MACAQUE
GREAT APES
SIAMANG
GORILLAS
ORANGUTANS

BABOONS
RHESUS MACAQUE
LESSER APES
CHIMPANZEES
BRACHIATION

Vocabulary Crossword
Lesson 6

Across

3. The most studied of all apes. They have large brains and exhibit great intelligence and curiosity about the world around them.
4. The largest of the primates, these animals are shy, docile and keep to themselves. The adult male defends his troop by beating his chest and charging the threatening creature.
6. Primates with long and sad-looking faces. Some scientists consider them the most intelligent primate, and they are the world's largest arboreal animals.
8. The group containing the gibbons. TWO WORDS
9. These primates tend to live in very large groups. They are generally brown or white with long, brown noses.
10. This monkey has a very big nose and lives only on the island of Boreno in Southeast Asia. TWO WORDS
12. The process of a primate swinging through the trees using its arms. Gibbons are masters of this kind of movement.
13. The group containing the larger apes. It includes chimpanzees, bonobos, gorillas and orangutans. TWO WORDS
15. The first primate in space. TWO WORDS

Down

1. These primates live in the rainforest and have colorful noses that are ridged.
2. These primates used to be called "pygmy chimpanzees." They spend more time walking upright and are less aggressive than chimpanzees.
5. The only monkey that can endure temperatures below freezing for long periods of time. Sometimes called the "snow monkey." TWO WORDS
7. Small apes that live in the rain forests. They have long fingers and arms and mark their territories by singing a duet with their mate from the highest trees.
11. The largest and darkest species of gibbon. It has an inflatable throat sac that acts like an amplifier for the vocal cords.
14. The less-colorful "cousin" of the mandrill. Its nose is black, and it is found only in Cameroon.

PRIMATES MINIBOOK
LESSON 6

Paste your Primates Wheel onto
this page.

Explore More
Lesson 6

DVD and Book Suggestions

Nature: Chimpanzees (1982) Narrated by Jane Goodall for PBS. Observe wild chimpanzees in their native habitat in Tanzania.

Nature: Koko (2004) Narrated by Martin Sheen for PBS. Investigates the ways in which Koko the gorilla communicates with the scientists who studied her.

Meet the Howlers by April Pulley Sayre (ages 4-8). A fun and lively picture book introduction to a family of monkeys.

Orangutan by Lynne Cherry (ages 4-8). A colorful picture book looks at orangutans in the rain forest as they swing through the treetops and care for their babies.

Rickie and Henri by Jane Goodall (ages 4-8). When her human guardian goes on a business trip, an orphaned chimpanzee infant adopts a shaggy dog as her "mother."

Slow Loris by Alexis Deacon (ages 4-8). An amusing picture book tale of a seemingly lethargic and boring loris living in a zoo.

Akimbo and the Baboons by Alexander McCall Smith (ages 6-9). Akimbo and his cousin Kosi accompany a scientist into the African bush to study the behavior of a troop of baboons.

Breakfast in the Rain Forest: A Visit with Mountain Gorillas by Richard Sobol (ages 6-9). Journey to the hidden habitat of and get an up-close look at mountain gorillas in the rain forests of Uganda.

Chimpanzee Roams the Forest by Gladys Plemon Conklin (ages 6-9). Follows one young chimpanzee's growth to adulthood.

Harvey's Marvelous Monkey Mystery by Eth Clifford (ages 6-9). Harvey, with the help of his cousin Nora, must solve a mystery when a monkey appears at his window one night.

Monkeys of Central and South America by Patricia A. Fink Martin (ages 6-9). Describes the physical characteristics, habitats, life cycles, and behavior of New World monkeys.

With Love by Jane Goodall (ages 6-9). A collection of stories based on the author's experiences with chimpanzees in Gombe Stream National Park in Tanzania over a period of almost forty years.

Among the Orangutans: The Birute Galdikas Story by Evelyn Gallardo (ages 9-12). Describes the life and research of Birute Galdikas, a prominent expert on the behavior of orangutans in the wild.

The Chimpanzee Family Book by Jane Goodall (ages 9-12). British naturalist Jane Goodall provides an intimate portrait of a group of chimpanzees she studied for many years in the jungles of Africa.

The Chimpanzees I Love: Saving Their World and Ours by Jane Goodall (ages 9-12). This renowned scientist and wildlife advocate shares the heroic story of her life with chimpanzees.

Friend Monkey by P.L. Travers (ages 9-12). The adventures of Monkey, from his departure from the jungle to his arrival in England where he makes many friends.

The Golden Lion Tamarin Comes Home by George Ancona (ages 9-12). Chronicles the steps biologists take to reintroduce tamarins into the wild.

Goodbye, Charley by Jane Buchanan (ages 9-12). In 1943, the gift of a rhesus monkey helps 12 year-old Celie deal with all the difficulties war has brought into her life in Gloucester, Massachusetts.

My Life with Chimpanzees by Jane Goodall (ages 9-12). The renowned English zoologist describes her early interest in animals and how it led to her study of chimpanzees in Tanzania.

Summer of the Monkeys by Wilson Rawls (ages 9-12). In the late 1800's, a fourteen-year-old Ozark mountain boy spends his summer trying to recapture monkeys that escaped from a traveling circus.

In Search of Lemurs by Joyce Ann Powzyk (ages 10-14). A researcher details her experiences studying the lemurs that inhabit the rain forests of Madagascar.

The Story of Doctor Dolittle by Hugh Lofting (ages 9-12). The adventures of a kind-hearted doctor who is fond of animals and understands their languages. He travels to Africa with some of his favorite pets to cure the monkeys of a terrible sickness.

MY PRIMATE PROJECT

Lesson 6

12/2/22

Depth Perception Experiment

What I did:

Object	Guessed Distance	Actual Distance	Difference
screen	15 ft.	19 ft. 4 in.	4 ft. 4 in.
dartboard	10 ft.	10 ft. 5 in.	5 in.
Eddie	7 ft. 3 in.	9 ft. 4 in.	2 ft. 1 in.

sample: glove to table   18" (18 in.)

high top table to fire pit   19' (19 ft.)

helmet to table   69" (69 in.) (5 ft. 9 in.)

What I learned:

Isaac learned he doesn't have as good depth perception as a primate and shouldn't jump from tree to tree. Also, everything was farther away than he thought.

FASCINATING FACTS

RODENTIA AND THE REST

Lesson 7

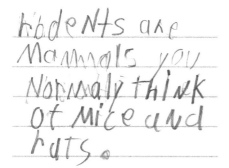

rodents are Mammals you Normaly think of Mice and ruts.

but there are many differanced rodents Like Shrews

beavehs and squirrels some rodents like squirrels have special abilities

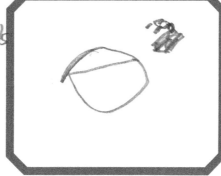

Like they can run across thees safely with out falling.

Name _____ Date _____

What Do You Remember?
Lesson 7 Review Questions

1. What is the main thing that makes an animal a rodent?

2. How are rodents helpful to the world?

3. How are they destructive?

4. Into what three groups do many scientists divide rodents?

5. Name three members of order Insectivora.

6. Which mammals are poisonous?

7. What are the differences among rabbits, hares and pikas?

8. Why are animals like the platypus and echidna difficult to classify as mammals?

9. How is the echidna like a marsupial?

10. Which animal in order Edentata really has no teeth?

11. What disease do armadillos sometimes carry?

12. How is an aardvark similar to an anteater?

13. Describe some differences between the two animals.

Mouse-Like Rodents

Squirrels

Beavers

Hedgehogs

Shrews

Rabbits

Pikas

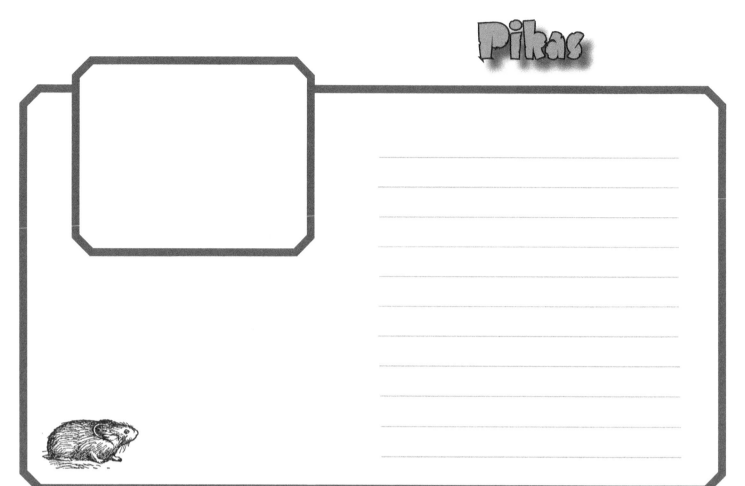

Colugos

Echidnas

Platypuses

Sloths

Anteaters

Armadillos

Aardvarks

My Creation

Of the animals that move about on the ground, these are unclean for you: the weasel, the rat, any kind of great lizard...

Leviticus 11:29

Of the animals that move about on the ground, these are unclean for you: the weasel, the rat, any kind of great lizard...

Leviticus 11:29

Vocabulary Crossword
Lesson 7

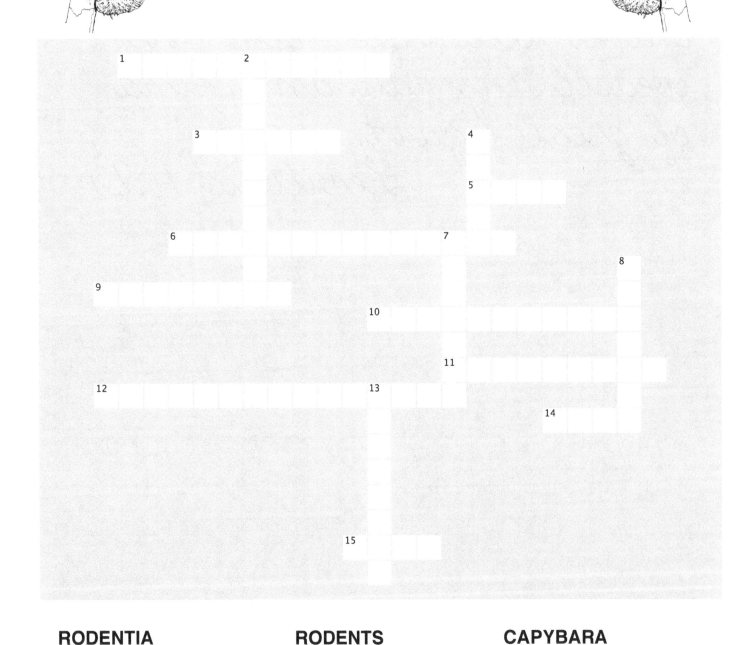

RODENTIA
BLACK PLAGUE
PTEROMYINI
DAMS
INSECTIVORA

RODENTS
DREY
BEAVERS
LODGE
SHREWS

CAPYBARA
FLYING SQUIRREL
KEYSTONE SPECIES
KITS
TREE SHREW

Vocabulary Crossword
Lesson 7

Across

1. A disease of the 1300s that was spread by rats and killed an estimated 75 million people. TWO WORDS
3. Small, secretive creatures that depend on their hearing and smell more than their vision. Some species have a poisonous bite.
5. Structures that beavers build to raise the water level so they can live more comfortably in the area where they have built their lodge.
6. This squirrel-like rodent is designed with extra skin flaps which can be used like an umbrella to glide from one tree to another. TWO WORDS
9. This order's name means "rodent."
10. The order where taxonomists put animals that usually eat insects and can't be put in any other order.
11. This animal looks a bit like a squirrel with a long, pointy nose and marks its territory with scents from special glands. It used to belong to the primate order. TWO WORDS
12. A species that other animals depend upon. TWO WORDS
14. A beaver's young.
15. A well-designed squirrel nest.

Down

2. What scientists call the many different species of flying squirrels.
4. A teepee-shaped pile of logs that beavers build as homes for their families.
7. With more than 2,000 species on every continent (with the exception of Antarctica) these animals make up about 40% of all mammals in the world. Their name means "gnaw tooth."
8. These animals are considered a keystone species and can actually change the entire landscape of the places of North America and Europe where they live.
13. The largest rodent living on the planet.

Vocabulary Crossword
Lesson 7

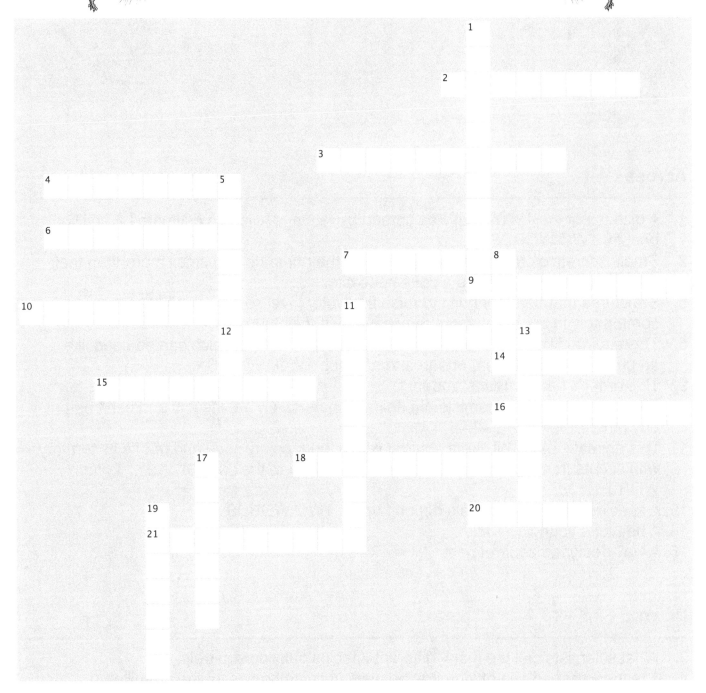

LAGOMORPHA	**RABBITS**	**HARES**	
PIKAS	**PRECOCIAL**	**ALTRICIAL**	
DERMOPTERA	**COLUGOS**	**PATAGIUM**	
MONOTREMATA	**PLATYPUS**	**ECHIDNA**	
EDENTATA	**SLOTH**	**SYMBIOTIC**	
ANTEATER	**ARMADILLO**	**AARDVARK**	
OVIPAROUS	**VIVIPAROUS**	**TUBULIDENTATA**	

Vocabulary Crossword
Lesson 7

Across

2. This animal uses its 2-foot-long tongue to scoop out food from nests. It walks on its knuckles and can grow to be 8 feet long.
3. The order to which rabbits belong. Its name means "hare-shaped" animal.
4. This animal looks like a cross between a beaver and a duck.
6. Skin that can stretch out like a parachute, enabling some animals to glide through the air.
7. These social lagomorphs are altricial and live in burrows under the ground.
9. Rabbits are born this way, with no fur and with their eyes closed.
10. An armored creature that dog-paddles long distances across wide rivers and lakes. It usually gives birth to four identical young.
12. The aardvark belongs to this order; its name means "tube-shaped teeth."
14. These lagomorphs have long ears and legs. Their nests are shallow depressions in the ground, and their young are born precocial.
15. Newborn hares are born this way. They have fur, and their eyes are open when they are born.
16. Sloths, anteaters and armadillos belong to this order.
18. This order's name means "skin wings."
20. Placed in the order lagomorpha, these creatures have short legs, short, round ears and no tail. They love cold temperatures and live on rocks or dig burrows in open meadows.
21. A term for egg-laying animals.

Down

1. The platypus and spiny anteater are the only members of this order.
5. When two or more creatures live together in a close relationship.
8. This animal's lazy lifestyle gives it its name. It has long, tough nails and spends 99% of its time in trees, often hanging upside down.
11. A term for animals that give birth to live young.
13. The Old World counterpart to the anteater. It has strong claws, thick skin and a flattened snout, like that of a pig.
17. Often called a spiny anteater, this creature looks like a cross between a bird, an anteater and a hedgehog.
19. Members of order Dermoptera that have the most extensive patagium in the world.

RODENTIA AND THE REST MINIBOOK
Lesson 7

Paste your Rodentia and the Rest
Animal Pocket onto this page.

Explore More
Lesson 7
Science Fair Fun

Develop a science fair project based on a question you might have about mice. For example, you might choose something from the following - or make one up of your own:

- What are the effects of music (rock and classical) on mice performance?
- Are humans more afraid of mice or snakes?
- Can mice run a race they memorized as quickly if they are hearing rock music?

Decide what you believe and formulate some ideas for testing your belief.

Here's a good resource to help you create a science fair project step by step: *Strategies for Winning Science Fair Projects* by Joyce Henderson and Heather Tomasello.

DVD and Book Suggestions

See How They Grow: Forest Animals by Dorling Kindersley, Inc. (all ages). Witness the growth of owls, mice, ants and chipmunks as they prepare for independent lives in a forest.

Mice Are Nice compiled by Nancy Larrick and Ed Young (all ages). A collection of poems about mice by David McCord, A. A. Milne, John Ciardi, Ian Serraillier, and others.

About Rodents: A Guide for Children by Cathryn P. Sill (ages 4-8). Simple text and delightful illustrations introduce young children to the world of rodents.

Animal Lives: The Rabbit by Sally Tagholm and Bert Kitchen (ages 4-8). Lovely illustrations and clear text narrate the life cycle of rabbits living in England.

Animals Do the Strangest Things by Leonora Hornblow (ages 4-8). Describes nineteen animals that have peculiar and strange characteristics, including the platypus that has poison spurs on its legs, the opossum that fools its enemies by pretending to be dead, and the bat that navigates by built-in sonar.

Armadillo Trail: The Northward Journey of the Armadillo by Stephen R. Swinburne (ages 4-8). Beautiful watercolor illustrations follow a female armadillo from her birth in the Texas landscape to a litter of her own in Kansas.

Beaver at Long Pond by William T. George and Lindsay Barrett George (ages 4-8). As the other animals at Long Pond settle down for the night, Beaver starts his nightly adventure.

Come Out Muskrats by Jim Arnosky (ages 4-8). Follow a pair of muskrats as they emerge from their home and swim, frolic, and eat at a pond and into the night.

Freckles the Rabbit by Jane Burton (ages 4-8). Follow a newborn rabbit throughout her first year of life.

A Mouse's Life by John Himmelman (ages 4-8). Using simple text and realistic illustrations, this book describes the daily activities and life cycle of a white-footed mouse.

Mouse Tail Moon by Joanne Rider (ages 4-8). A series of poems and illustrations depict the world of a field mouse from sundown to sunup.

Night Rabbits by Lee Posey (ages 4-8). Delightfully illustrated, this book tells how a young girl tries to help when the rabbits she loves start eating her father's prized lawn.

Prize in the Snow by Jim Easterling (ages 4-8). A young boy sets out one winter day to become a great hunter, but his plans change when he traps a starving rabbit.

Rabbits and Raindrops by Jim Arnosky (ages 4-8). Gentle watercolors depict five baby rabbits as they hop out of their nest for the very first time and meet their animal neighbors.

Sadie the Shrew by Gisela Buck (ages 4-8). Follows the everyday life of a female shrew as it cares for its babies.

Scamper: A Gray Tree Squirrel by Edna Miller (ages 4-8). A little gray tree squirrel struggles to protect itself from predators, build a nest, and find food.

Squirrels by Brian Wildsmith (ages 4-8). Using fantastic illustrations and informative text, the everyday lives of squirrels are exposed in a beautiful way.

Tom Crean's Rabbit: A True Story from Scott's Last Voyage by Meredith Hooper (ages 4-8). A sailor's search for a nest for his pet rabbit spurs a fascinating tour aboard a ship headed toward Antarctica in 1910.

*Be aware that some titles may contain evolutionary content   125

The Wild Woods by Simon James (ages 4-8). While walking in the woods, a young girl spies a squirrel and wants to make it her pet, against her grandfather's objections.

A Look Through the Mouse Hole by Heiderose Fischer-Nagel (ages 6-9). Photographs and simple text examine the behavior of a family of mice living in a basement, comparing their habits to those of outdoor mice.

Beavers Beware! by Barbara Brenner (ages 6-9). A family with a house on the river finds two beavers cutting down trees and building a lodge on their dock.

Bony by Frances W. Zweifel (ages 6-9). When his squirrel creates havoc as a house pet, Kim teaches Bony to be an outside squirrel.

Lucky Mouse by Elizabeth Ring (ages 6-9). Using photographs and simple text, this story tells how one abandoned deer mouse is rescued by children and placed into the nest of a white-footed mouse.

The Moon of the Chickarees by Jean Craighead George (ages 6-9). Follow the lives of five squirrel pups as they are taught to fend for themselves in the Cumberland Valley of Pennsylvania.

The Moon of the Moles by Jean Craighead George (ages 6-9). Follow a young mole in Kansas as it searches for food in its network of underground tunnels.

A Platypus, Probably by Sneed B. Collard (ages 6-9). Follow a female platypus as she hunts for food, finds a mate, builds a shelter, and cares for her pups.

A Platypus' World by Caroline Arnold (ages 6-9). Bold cut-paper illustrations and informative text introduce children to the life cycle and habits of the platypus.

All Keyed Up by Matt Christopher (ages 7-10). When soccer teammate and new friend Stookie asks Jerry to care for his gerbils while he is on vacation, Jerry happily agrees; then disaster strikes.

Bubonic Plague by Jim Whiting (ages 7-10). Recounts the course and cause of the terrible disease that swept Europe, Asia, and North Africa in the 14th century.

Prairie Dogs by Emery Bernhard (ages 7-10). An abundance of information coupled with delightful illustrations results in a balanced yet gentle introduction to the life cycle and habits of the prairie dog.

Prairie Dog Summer by Faith McNulty (ages 7-10). While helping his uncle study prairie dogs, Paul discovers wild animals are good for something besides target practice.

The Song of the Christmas Mouse by Shirley Rousseau Murphy (ages 7-10). A boy's efforts to capture a wild mouse for a pet seem constantly thwarted by his willful younger cousin who has come to stay for Christmas.

Beaver of Weeping Water by Marian Rumsey (ages 9-12). When his father is away and an industrious beaver starts building a dam that cuts off the valley's water supply, Joey must decide how to dispose of the animal.

The Black Death by Louise Chipley Slavicek (ages 9-12). Recounts the course and cause of the terrible disease that swept Europe, Asia, and North Africa in the 14th century.

Chipmunks on the Doorstep by Edwin Tunis (ages 9-12). Relates the author's observations of the habits of the backyard chipmunks that became his pets.

Henry by Nina Bawden (ages 9-12). Evacuated to the English countryside during World War II, a fatherless family tries to raise a baby squirrel that also lost its home.

Incident at Hawk's Hill by Allan W. Eckert (ages 9-12) Newberry Honor Book. A shy, lonely six-year-old wanders into the Canadian prairie and spends a summer under the protection of a badger.

Miss Pickerell and the Lost World by Dora F. Pantell (ages 9-12). When a flood in Square Toe Country washes in a strange creature, Miss Pickerell goes on a perilous journey to return it to its native habitat.

A Mouse Named Mus by Irene Brady (ages 9-12). A young boy's pet mouse is faced with a life-or-death struggle for survival when it escapes from the house into the woods.

Nuts: A Novel by Kacy Cook (ages 9-12). A young girl finds an abandoned baby squirrel in her backyard and convinces her parents to let her raise it as a pet, and then things go very wrong.

Shadrach by Meinert De Jong (ages 9-12). Newberry Honor Book. Davie's pet rabbit disappears despite the loving care bestowed on it.

Beaver Skins and Mountain Men: The Importance of the Beaver in the Discovery, Exploration, and Settlement of the North American Continent by Carl Burger (ages 10+). Discusses the influence the craze for beaver had on the development and exploration of North America and describes the men attracted by the opportunity for profit and adventure.

Squirrels and Other Furbearers by John Burroughs (ages 10+). Anecdotes based on the author's firsthand observations and personal encounters with these creatures of the wild.

My Rodents Project

Lesson 7

What I did: i disected a owl pellet to see if i could cind hodentsbone and piece them together

What I learned: i learned that its not as easy as i thoutg to disesct a owl pellet and iddentify what roden it was. i found a hat skull it looks ont of like this.

FASCINATING FACTS ABOUT Ungulates
Lesson 8

UNgulates
are animals
like farms,
animals

one ungulates the elephant
is one of the biggest
ungulates

128

Name _____ Date _____

1. What are the different uses for an elephant's proboscis? shaking hands slapping predors

2. Why do elephants blow dust? to take a bath

3. How are mammoths like elephants? Dotn have tucks and like he

4. How are they different? mammoths have fur

5. How do mammoths help us understand how the Ice Age might have happened?

6. In what kind of habitat did the mastodon live?
cold areas

7. How are horses and ponies different?
horses are bigger then ponnies

8. What does it mean when a horse is labeled hot-, cold-, or warm-blooded?
some horses are cold or hot blood

9. Identify the following: filly, colt, foal, stallion, mare, and yearling.
filly

10. Explain the main differences between donkeys and horses.

11. How are zebra stripes like your fingerprints?

12. How are zebras like donkeys?

13. Why are rhinoceroses endangered?

14. Of what is a rhino's horn made?

15. How are tapirs like elephants?

16. How are they like pigs?

Elephants

Take dust
batns. By blowi
ng dust on them.
the heare 3
diffent species
of elephants

Horses

there are plenty of wild horse in the wild today all over the western part of the united states these horses are descended from feral horse

Donkeys

donkeys
are smaller
the horses
with lager
ears and a
loud voice
there move
is stiff. A
male donkey
is usseally
called a
Jack

Zebras

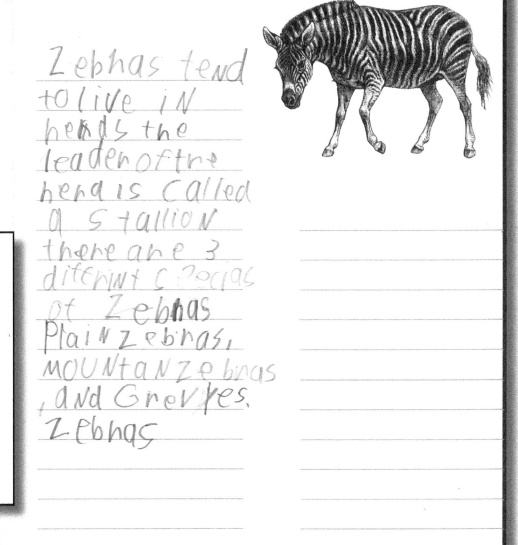

Zebras tend to live in herds the leader of the herd is called a stallion there are 3 diferint species of Zebras Plain Zebras, Mountan Zebras, and Grevyes. Zebras

Rhinos

rhinos have 3 toes rhinos
can sometime grow 14 feet long
and weaigh as much as 4 tons
there are 5 species of rhinos
black and white rhinos indian
rhino (+) javan rhino sumatran rhino

Tapirs

they are shape short of like
a large pig they live in
rainforest althouth many
live in hy hot places they
are shy

Odd-toed Ungulates Quiz

1. TRUE ☐ FALSE ☐ _____

2. TRUE ☐ FALSE ☐ _____

3. TRUE ☐ FALSE ☐ _____

4. TRUE ☐ FALSE ☐ _____

5. TRUE ☐ FALSE ☐ _____

6. TRUE ☐ FALSE ☐ _____

7. TRUE ☐ FALSE ☐ _____

8. TRUE ☐ FALSE ☐ _____

9. TRUE ☐ FALSE ☐ _____

10. TRUE ☐ FALSE ☐ _____

11. TRUE ☐ FALSE ☐ _____

12. TRUE ☐ FALSE ☐ _____

"Do not be afraid, O Daughter of Zion;
see, your king is coming, seated on a
donkey's colt."

John 12:15

"Do not be afraid, O Daughter of Zion; see, your king is coming, seated on a donkey's colt."

John 12:15

Vocabulary Crossword
Lesson 8

LIVESTOCK
PACHYDERMS
ASIAN ELEPHANT
GEYSER
PERISSODACTYLA
FERAL
JOG
CANTER
FOAL
COLT
GELDING
HINNEY

UNGULATES
TUSKS
MATRIARCH
ICE AGE
EQUIDAE
GAIT
GALLOP
PONY
YEARLING
MARE
DONKEY
TROT

PROBOSCIDEA
AFRICAN BUSH ELEPHANT
AFRICAN FOREST ELEPHANT
WOOLY MAMMOTHS
MASTODONS
HOT-BLOODED HORSES
COLD-BLOODED HORSES
WARM-BLOODED HORSES
FILLY
STALLION
MULE
WALK

Vocabulary Crossword
Lesson 8

Across

5. When a female donkey mates with a male horse she gives birth to this animal.
7. Now extinct, these animals resemble the mammoth. They lived in forests, eating mostly twigs and leaves. Some even had four tusks.
9. Animals whose ancestors were originally domesticated but turned wild.
10. Any horse that is between one and two years old.
14. Elephants belong to this order.
17. A three-beat gait that is faster than a trot. It starts with a hind foot hitting the ground.
18. Elephants have these "tools" which they use to help retrieve food and defend themselves.
21. Horses that are smaller and built for speed, like Arabians and thoroughbreds. THREE WORDS
22. When a female horse mates with a male donkey she gives birth to this animal.
24. This elephant grows 9 feet high and lives in the forests of Africa. THREE WORDS
25. A very slow trot.
27. Animals in this order have a large middle toe that defines the center of the foot.
30. An equine that is less than 14.2 hands tall.
31. The way in which a horse walks or runs.
33. Animals with hooves.

Down

1. Animals that help people with their work or give them food.
2. A fully grown female horse.
3. No longer in existence, these large animals were covered with long hair and had tusks that curled upward. They lived in open plains, grazing on grass and flowers. TWO WORDS
4. What we call larger, gentler horses that have been bred for working and hauling. These include draft horses and Clydesdales. THREE WORDS
6. The horse family. It also includes donkeys, zebras, kulans and kiangs.
8. One of the horse's gaits; the horse is suspended in the air for a moment in every stride.
9. A female horse that isn't fully grown.
11. Living on the plains of Africa, this elephant is usually 12 feet high. THREE WORDS
12. The medium-sized horses. They are the favorite for horse riding competitions and shows and include quarter horses and paints. THREE WORDS
13. A male horse that isn't fully grown.
15. This elephant has small ears and only the male has tusks. Its head has more hair than that of other elephants. TWO WORDS
16. The slowest and steadiest gait of a horse. Two or three hooves are on the ground at all times.
19. The fastest of the horse's standard gaits; it is a four-beat gait.
20. Any horse that isn't a year old yet.
22. The head of an elephant herd; the oldest and most experienced female.
23. "Thick-skinned" creatures, like elephants.
26. An adult male horse that has been neutered to make it calmer and more obedient.
28. A fully grown male horse.
29. This equine has a stiff, upright mane and a tail like a cow's tail.
31. A place where an opening allows water from deep under the earth to spew up onto the earth's surface.
32. A time when the entire earth was, on average, cooler than normal. TWO WORDS

Vocabulary Crossword
Lesson 8

ZEBRA
TAPIRS
RHINO
TICK BIRDS
BLACK RHINO
JAVAN RHINO
INDIAN RHINO
WHITE RHINO
SUMATRAN RHINO

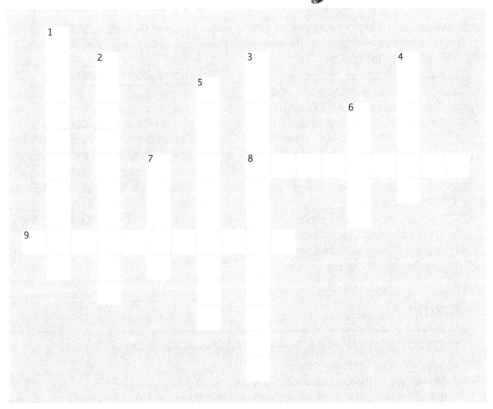

Across

8. Another name for oxpeckers. These birds warn rhinos of lurking danger and eat parasites that live on the rhino's skin. TWO WORDS
9. This rhino lives in India and Nepal. TWO WORDS

Down

1. The second largest terrestrial mammal, next to the elephant. TWO WORDS
2. A species of rhino with two horns that is not hairy and not the second largest terrestrial mammal. TWO WORDS
3. A small, hairy rhino with two horns. It lives in the dense rain forests and mountains of Southeast Asia. TWO WORDS
4. These animals looks like a cross between a pig and an elephant. They have a proboscis that they use as a snorkel.
5. This rhino lives in Indonesia and Vietnam. TWO WORDS
6. An animal that is similar to the horse and donkey. It has a unique stripe pattern covering its body.
7. A large, three-toed animal with thick, lumpy skin and at least one big horn on the front of its head.

UNGULATES MINIBOOKS
Lesson 8

Paste your Ungulates Miniature
Books onto this page.

UNGULATES MINIBOOKS
Lesson 8

Paste your Ungulates Miniature
Books onto this page.

Explore More
Lesson 8

DVD and Book Suggestions

Black Beauty (1994) distributed by Warner Home Video. Stunning adaptation of the classic novel by Anna Sewell.

The Black Stallion (1979) distributed by MGM. An Academy Award nominated adaptation of the classic novel by Walter Farely.

Danny (1977) distributed by Janson Media. A young girl nurses and rehabilitates a cute gray pony named Danny who is discarded by the spoiled daughter of a barn owner.

Ride a Wild Pony (1975) distributed by Disney. A treasured pony means freedom to two very different children but can only belong to one.

National Velvet (1945) distributed by Warner Home Video. Young Elizabeth Taylor became a movie star after starring in this classic about a girl and her jockey pal who transform an unruly horse into a champion.

Nature: Africa's Incredible Hulks (2007) distributed by PBS. Details the survival tactics of both the elephant and the rhinoceros on the wild African plain.

Nature: Cloud, Wild Stallion of the Rockies (2003) distributed by PBS. Follows a colt for over nine years as it grows into a stallion in the mountains of Montana and examines the odds it had to beat to do so, being born with a coat of pure white.

Nature: Echo of Elephants (2005) Hosted by Cynthia Moss for PBS. Follows mother elephant Echo and her remarkable herd of pachyderms in Kenya's Amboseli National Park.

Nature: Horses (1982) Narrated by Julia Roberts for PBS; Emmy Winner. Examines the complex relationship between rider and horse.

The Silver Stallion (1998) distributed by Lion's Gate. Follow the struggle of wild horses in the Australian bush when men come to catch and break them.

The Story of Sea Biscuit (1949) distributed by Warner Home Video. A loose retelling of the true story of an underdog champion.

The Blind Colt by Glen Rounds (ages 4-8). A blind colt roams with a band of mustangs, but is eventually adopted and trained as a saddle horse by ten-year-old Whitey.

Home Now by Lesley Beake (ages 4-8). After the death of her parents, young Sieta goes to live with her aunt on the other side of the mountains in Africa, but she is sad and lonely until she meets a young elephant.

Little Big Ears: The Story of Ely by Cynthia Moss (ages 4-8). A photo essay follows the first year in an elephant's life as it struggles to survive in the African plains after having been born with defective legs.

Once We Had a Horse by Glen Rounds (ages 4-8). In this autobiographical picture book, a family of children spends its summer playing with an old horse on a ranch in Montana.

A Zebra's World by Caroline Arnold (ages 4-8). A boldly illustrated picture book packed with facts about the life cycle and habits of zebras.

Akimbo and the Elephants by Alexander McCall Smith (ages 6-9). On the African game preserve where his father works, Akimbo devises a dangerous plan to capture a ring of elephant poachers.

Bonny's Big Day by James Herriot (ages 6-9). Farmer Skipton is persuaded to enter his old carthorse in the Darrowby Pet Show.

The Burro That Ran Away by Wilma Pitchford Hays (ages 6-9). A boy's efforts to be friends with a runaway burro include tracking it down after it mysteriously escapes from the corral.

Changes for Kaya: A Story of Courage by Janet Beeler Shaw (ages 6-9). While searching for the horse stolen from her, Kaya faces danger from a sudden mountain fire.

Meet Kaya: An American Girl by Janey Beeler Shaw (ages 6-9). In 1764, when Kaya and her family reunite with other Nez Perce Indians to fish for red salmon, she learns that bragging, even about her swift horse, can lead to trouble.

The Treasure of Topo-el-Bampo by Scott O'Dell (ages 6-9). Two burros, sold to the slave-driving owners of a silver mine, eventually return to save their village from starvation.

The Useless Donkeys by Lydia Pender (ages 6-9). The Quigley children love their two donkeys, but Mr. Quigley threatens to get rid of them because they are useless.

The White Stallion by Elizabeth Shub (ages 6-9). In 1845, a young girl is carried away from her wagon train and befriended by a wild stallion.

Winter's Gift by Jane Monroe Donovan (ages 7+). On Christmas Eve, an old farmer whose wife has died acquires new hope after helping a pregnant mare during a snowstorm.

Explore More
Lesson 8

The Blind Connemara by C.W. Anderson (ages 7-10). A young girl is determined that her pony's blindness is not going to keep him from earning the blue ribbon in a horse show.

Conquista! by Clyde Robert Bulla (ages 7-10). At the time of Coronado's exploration for a fabled city of gold, a young Native American boy encounters his first horse.

Our Own Pony by Marguerite Henry (ages 7-10). Two twin brothers discover the joys and pains of horse ownership when they purchase and raise a pony that foals, giving them more responsibility than they expected.

They Had a Horse by Walter D. Edmonds (ages 7-10). A poor pioneer family purchases an old nag and receives a delightful surprise.

Wild Appaloosa by Glen Rounds (ages 7-10). A handsome Appaloosa filly, desired by wild horse hunters, makes a young boy's dream come true.

Uncovering the Wooly Mammoth by Michael & Beverly Oard (ages 8-11). Provides Biblical and scientific reasons for the wooly mammoth's disappearance at the end of the Ice Age.

The Black Stallion by Walter Farley (ages 9-12). The classic story of a boy shipwrecked on an island with a stallion.

Born to Trot by Marguerite Henry (ages 9-12). Young Gib dreams of having his own filly Rosalind become a champion trotter.

Brighty of the Grand Canyon by Marguerite Henry (ages 9-12). Relates the adventures of a little burro that blazed trails through the Grand Canyon and met many famous people in the process.

In the Village of the Elephants by Jeremy Schmidt (ages 9-12). Follow a typical day in the life of a young mahout (elephant trainer) in Southern India.

The Island of Horses by Eilis Dillon (ages 9-12). When two boys from a remote island off the western Irish coast venture to the forbidden Island of Horses, they find a mysteriously tame black colt and unexpected danger.

Justin Morgan Had a Horse by Marguerite Henry (ages 9-12). An unusual workhorse raised in Vermont becomes the sire of a famous American breed.

King of the Wind: The Story of the Godolphin Arabian by Marguerite Henry (ages 9-12) Newberry Medal Winner. Sham the stallion and a stable boy travel from Morocco to France to England where, at last, Sham's majesty is recognized.

Little Arliss by Fred Gipson (ages 9-12). A small twelve-year old boy's determination to prove he is tough sets him on the trail of a runaway horse.

Little Britches: Father and I Were Ranchers by Ralph Moody (ages 9-12). In 1906, a young boy moves with his family from New Hampshire to a ranch in Colorado and experiences both the strains and the rewards of hard work.

Misty of Chincoteague by Marguerite Henry (ages 9-12). Paul and his sister Maureen are determined to own a pony from the herd on Chincoteague Island, Virginia when the Phantom and her colt are among the wild ponies rounded up for the yearly auction.

A Morgan for Melinda by Doris Gates (ages 9-12). Through her friendship with an elderly writer, 10-year-old Melinda overcomes her fear of riding horses.

My Friend Flicka by Mary O'Hara (ages 9-12). Through his intense devotion to a colt named Flicka, a young boy living on a Wyoming ranch learns about responsibility and gains a better understanding of his rough father.

Stormy, Misty's Foal by Marguerite Henry (ages 9-12). The true story of the foal born during the aftermath of a terrible storm that nearly destroyed Chincoteague Island.

Thunderhead by Mary O'Hara (ages 9-12). An exciting tale about a boy with high hopes for his racehorse.

National Velvet by Enid Bagnold (ages 10+). The classic story about spirited Velvet Brown and her beloved horse.

Black Beauty by Anna Sewell (ages 9-12). A horse in nineteenth-century England recounts its experiences with both good and bad masters.

Smoky the Cowhorse by Will James (ages 9-12) Newberry Medal Book. Told from the animal's perspective, this is the story of Smoky, a wild horse born on the open range and later broken by man.

My Ungulates Project
Lesson 8

What I did:

What I learned:

FASCINATING FACTS

ABOUT

Artiodactyla

Lesson 9

are even numbered unglutes. You can find some on a farm and som out in the wild

some have twin hohns sometime their curved

FASCINATING FACTS

ABOUT

Artiodactyla

Lesson 9

Name _isaac King_   Date _MON, JaN.30_

What Do You Remember?
Lesson 9 Review Questions

1. What is rumination? chew a chew oven again

2. Are deer a part of the antelope group? yes

3. Which animals migrate with wildebeests? gazels and zebhas

4. What do impalas do when they are frightened or startled? they stant to JUMP

5. Where are zebu cattle found?

6. Tell the basic history of bison. the bison was anumehous UNTil they wene almost hunted to extinc

7. What special features do camels have that enable them to survive in the desert? they through up and eat it

8. Why might you find a set of antlers with no deer attached? because they shed theih antlers

9. How do giraffes give evidence for our Creator? the highest blood phe sche w

10. How did God protect the Israelites by telling them not to eat pig meat? because the pigs canhy a disies

11. How are peccaries different from pigs?

12. Which is the most dangerous animal in Africa? hippos

My Zoo Project
Exhibits

God blessed them and said to them, "Be fruitful and increase in number; fill the earth and subdue it. Rule over the fish of the sea and the birds of the air and over every living creature that moves on the ground."

Genesis 1:28

God blessed them and said to them, "Be fruitful and increase in number; fill the earth and subdue it. Rule over the fish of the sea and the birds of the air and over every living creature that moves on the ground." Genesis 1:28

God blessed them and said to them, "Be fruitful and increase in number; fill the earth and subdue it. Rule over the fish of the sea and the birds of the air and over every living creature that moves on the ground."

Genesis 1:28

Vocabulary Crossword
Lesson 9

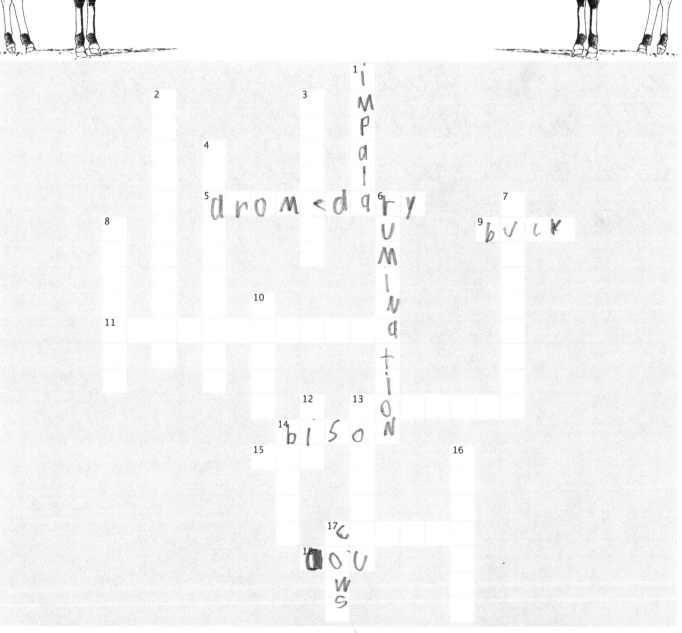

Across/Down answers filled in:
- 1 (down): impala
- 5 (across): dromedary
- 6 (down): rumination
- 9 (across): buck
- 14 (across): bison
- 17 (down): c
- 18 (across): cows

Word list:

ARTIODACTYLA	~~RUMINATION~~	~~RUMINANTS~~
CUD	CATTLE	~~COWS~~
~~BULLS~~	BOVIDAE	GAZELLE
~~IMPALA~~	BUFFALO	WILDEBEESTS
BOVINES	~~BUCK~~	~~BISON~~
KID	CAMEL	DOE
DUIKERS	INDIGENOUS	~~DROMEDARY~~

Vocabulary Crossword
Lesson 9

Across

5. A common species of camel that has only one hump.
9. A male caprine. Also called a "billy."
11. The animals in this order don't have a middle toe.
13. A group of large, slow grazers, including buffalo, bison, cattle and yaks.
14. These large, dark animals were at one time nearly extinct. Native Americans killed them for their hides, meat and bones. They are typically found in Colorado, Montana and Canada, and their meat is served in certain restaurants.
15. A partially digested ball of food.
17. The term used to refer to both male and female bovines.
18. A female caprine. Also called a "nanny."

Down

1. This animal lives on the African plain and can jump more than 8 feet into the air and land more than 30 feet from where it started.
2. These large, dark animals have horns with no ridges and a mane. They migrate in a continual, clockwise pattern over the eastern and southern plains of Africa.
3. Shy, deer-like animals that are native to Africa. They dive for cover whenever anyone is around.
4. A word that means "native to."
6. The process of chewing your food and swallowing it, only to have it come back up your throat and into your mouth to be chewed and swallowed again.
7. Animals that eat by way of rumination.
8. Bison are often mistakenly called this.
10. An animal created for life in the hot, sandy parts of the world.
12. A baby goat.
13. Cattle belong to this family, as do antelopes, gazelles, goats and sheep.
14. Male cattle.
16. This animal is similar to an antelope. It can run for a long time without getting tired.
17. Female cattle.

Vocabulary Crossword
Lesson 9

CERVIDAE
MOOSE
MASAI GIRAFFES
SUIDAE
SOUNDERS
PECCARIES
JAVELINA

MUSK DEER
REINDEER
RETICULATED GIRAFFES
SOW
WARTHOG
RAZORBACKS
HIPPOPOTAMUS

MUSK
GIRAFFES
OKAPI
BOARS
TRICHINOSIS
ALTRUISM

Vocabulary Crossword
Lesson 9

Across

1. Deer belong to this family.
3. A collection of several species of deer that produces an extremely powerful scent. TWO WORDS
5. This creature, found throughout Texas, has razor-sharp tusks that it uses to defend itself and attack its prey. Its name means "javelin" or "sword," and its favorite food is cactus.
6. A disease that is caused by eating pork that has been infested with a kind of worm. It can be fatal.
8. The only deer species in which the females also have antlers. They are often called caribou in North America.
9. This animal looks like a cross between a giraffe and a zebra. It has special features that enable it to live in the rain forest.
11. This massive, 11-foot long, 5,000 pound creature is the most feared animal in Africa. It can both float in the water and sink down to the bottom.
12. These creatures are similar to pigs, but they have long skinny legs and tusks that grow straight down. They have a powerful musk gland on top of their rump, and their odor gets worse when they are mad or excited.
14. The tallest of all God's creatures alive today. They have very long necks and tongues.
16. These giraffes have spots shaped a lot like rectangles. TWO WORDS
18. Groups of sows (female pigs) and their offspring that live in the wild.
19. Male pigs.

Down

2. When a person or animal behaves with unselfish concern for others.
3. These giraffes from Kenya have spots with jagged edges. TWO WORDS
4. This animal is typically found on the outskirts of forests in Africa. It wallows in the mud when it's hot and often sleeps in aardvark holes.
7. Members of this family are often called swine. Domesticated pigs, warthogs and forest hogs are in this family.
10. Part of family Cervidae, these animals represent its largest members.
13. The only wild pigs in the New World. They are once-domesticated pigs that went feral.
15. A scent produced by musk deer. It is used in perfumes and natural medicines.
17. A female pig.

ARTIODACTYLS MINIBOOK
Lesson 9

Paste your Artiodactyls
Minibook onto this page

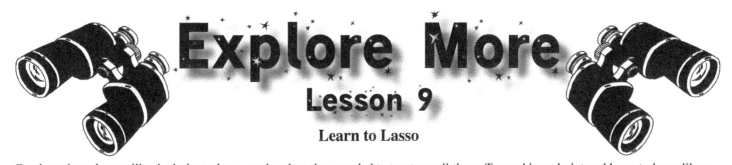

Explore More
Lesson 9
Learn to Lasso

Cowboys have long utilized a lariat to lasso cattle when they needed to treat or sell them. Try making a lariat and learn to lasso like a real cowboy! You'll need a rope and an object to lasso. Here's how to make a lariat: slip the rope through the small loop at the end of the lariat. Next, form a loop about one to two feet in diameter. Hold the loop lightly in your right hand a foot or so from the small loop at the end of the rope. Coil the rest of the lariat in your left hand leaving 5 to 6 feet of rope between the large loop and the coil. Now stand in front of a target. You can use a bale of hay with a long stick wedged in it. The bale will not tip over easily. You can also make some "horns" by placing two sturdy pieces of wood in front of the bale. Now, begin to slowly swing the rope over your head, right to left. Think of the lariat's loop as a wheel revolving horizontally over your head. Toss the loop by swinging your arm quickly forward bringing your wrist down to shoulder level while extending your arm out. Be careful not to interfere with the motion of the lariat. Now open your hand and toss the loop toward the target, keeping it straight and level. Try your best to maintain a smooth and steady rhythm as you toss the loop. The distance your lariat will travel depends on the amount of force you use when thrusting the loop forward. To finish, pull the lariat coiled in your left hand and tighten the loop around your target.

Dissect a Cow or Sheep Brain, Heart or Eye

Dissection is a great way to learn animal anatomy and physiology. When you purchase a specimen to dissect, you will also need to get an instruction manual and the supplies for the dissection. You can purchase preserved specimens from the following science supply companies: www.hometrainingtools.com, www.nilesbio.com, www.carolina.com, www.wardsci.com.

DVD and Book Suggestions

Nature: Holy Cows (2004) Narrated by Edward Hermann for PBS. Explores the scientific, agricultural and nutritional significance of the everyday cow.

Nature: Tall Blondes (2004) Narrated by Lynn Sherr for PBS. Learn all there is to know from the experts about the giraffe.

Nature: Prince of the Alps (2008) distributed by PBS. Together, a mother and young stag fight a difficult battle for survival along ancient migration paths in the forests and mountains of the Alps.

All About Deer by Jim Arnosky (ages 4-8). Compares the deer that inhabit North and Central America, including information about their life cycles, eating habits, and habitats.

Beatrice's Goat by Page McBrier (ages 4-8). A young girl's dream of attending school in her small Ugandan village is realized after her family is given an income-producing goat.

The Buffalo Are Back by Jean Craighead George (ages 4-8). A picture book tells the dramatic story of the bison's return from near-extinction in North America.

Buffalo Days by Diane Hoyt-Goldsmith (ages 4-8). Describes life on a Crow Indian reservation in Montana, focusing on the importance these tribes place on buffalo, which are again thriving in areas where the Crow live.

Buffalo Music by Tracey E. Fern (ages 4-8). Based on a true story, a woman raises orphaned buffalo calves found near her Texan home and eventually ships four members of her small herd to Yellowstone National Park, where they form the beginnings of now thriving buffalo herds.

Buffalo Thunder by Patricia Wittmann (ages 4-8). A young boy travels west by wagon train with his family and, although he experiences much, longs to see buffalo.

A Caribou Journey by Debbie S. Miller (ages 4-8). A picture book that examines the habitat, characteristics, and habits of a herd of caribou living in Alaska.

A Giraffe Grows Up by Amanda Doering Tourville (ages 4-8). A picture book that follows the growth of a giraffe on the African savannah.

Love from Uncle Clyde by Nancy Winslow Parker (ages 4-8). A little boy receives a hippopotamus for his birthday from his Uncle Clyde in Africa with instructions on how to take care of it.

A Mama for Owen by Marion Dane Bauer (ages 4-8). A picture book based on the true story of a baby hippopotamus who, when separated from its mother during the Indian Ocean Tsunami of 2004, bonds with a giant tortoise.

Milk: From Cow to Carton by Aliki (ages 4-8). Takes young children on an informative tour, following the trail of milk and milk products' production.

The Milk Makers by Gail Gibbons (ages 4-8). Follow the milk trail from farm to table: what cows must eat to produce healthy milk, and the process milk must go through before it reaches our homes.

Old Crump: A True Story of a Trip West by Laurie Lawlor (ages 4-8). In 1850, a faithful ox helps a family survive its trip through Death Valley, west to California.

The Snow Lambs by Debi Gliori (ages 4-8). As a winter storm approaches, a family's sheepdog is thought missing, but it's actually on a rescue mission for a pregnant ewe.

Blossom Comes Home by James Herriot (ages 6-9). To make room for a younger cow, Farmer Dakin reluctantly takes his old cow Blossom to market with surprising results.

Deer in the Pasture by Donald Carrick (ages 6-9). When hunting season arrives, a deer that has become too friendly with man must be frightened and driven away for its own protection.

The Goat Lady by Jane Bregoli (ages 6-9). Tells the story of an eccentric and elderly French-Canadian woman living in Massachusetts who raised goats to provide milk for anyone who needed it.

The King's Giraffe by Mary Jo Collier (ages 6-9). When the pasha of Egypt sends his friend, the king of France, a magnificent giraffe the people of France are awed and impressed, having never before seen such a creature.

Mary was a Little Lamb by Gloria Rand (ages 6-9). Based on a true story, an abandoned and troublesome lamb is adopted by a woman who eventually must place it in a petting zoo.

The Moon of the Deer by Jean Craighead George (age 6-9). A young buck weathers a hurricane that strikes the coast of Connecticut.

The Moon of the Wild Pigs by Jean Craighead George (ages 6-9). Follow the adventures of a lone peccary piglet as it investigates its desert surroundings in Arizona.

Shag: Last of the Plains Buffalo by Robert M. McClung (ages 6-9). Narrates the daily struggle of a buffalo against famine, drought, and death by hunters in the days when bison moved in mighty herds on America's plains.

Stella's Bull by Frances C. Arrington (ages 6-9). Young Mary Wilson comes face to face with her greatest fear when a boy throws her spelling book into Stella's pasture.

What About Emma? by Ken Rush (ages 6-9). Sue's family quits the dairy business, selling all the cows except Emma, Sue's favorite, because she is going to calf soon.

A Llama in the Family by Johanna Hurwitz (ages 7-10). Hoping for a mountain bike, a young boy is only momentarily disappointed by his mother's surprise.

A Moose for Jessica by Pat A. Wakefield (ages 7-10). Recounts the true story of how one wild moose bull wandered onto a farm in Vermont and developed an attachment to one of the cows living there.

Owen and Mzee: The True Story of a Remarkable Friendship by Isabella Hatkoff (ages 7-10). The true story of a baby hippopotamus who, separated from its mother during the Indian Ocean Tsunami of 2004, bonds with a giant tortoise.

Owen and Mzee: The Language of Friendship by Isabella Hatkoff (ages 7-10). Continues the story of the unique friendship between an orphaned hippo and a 130-year-old tortoise.

Tracker by Gary Paulson (ages 7-10). Only thirteen, John must track a deer in the Minnesota woods for his family's winter meat, but finds himself drawn to the doe that leads him.

Being Caribou: Five Months on Foot with a Caribou Herd by Karsten Heuer (ages 9-12). Through photographs and engaging text, the author recounts how he and his wife followed on foot a herd of caribou during its summer migration to Arctic birthing grounds. (Adapted for children from an adult text of the same name.)

Frankie and the Fawn by Marcia Polese (ages 9-12). An injured fawn has the good fortune of being found by two youngsters whose mother is a veterinarian.

Me, My Goat, and My Sister's Wedding by Stella Pevsner (ages 9-12). Doug and his friends keep a pet goat a secret from their families, but before long sightings of the high-spirited animal occur at very inappropriate places.

Water Buffalo Days: Growing Up in Vietnam by Quang Nhuong Huynh (ages 9-12). The author recounts his childhood in Vietnam, focusing on his relationship with his family's two water buffalo.

The Yearling by Marjorie Kinnan Rawlings (ages 10+) Pulitzer Prize Winner. A young boy living in the Florida backwoods is forced to decide the fate of a fawn he lovingly raised as a pet.

Bambi by Felix Salten (ages 9-12). The realistic adventures of a young deer in the forest as it grows into a beautiful stag.

Charlotte's Web by E.B. White (ages 9-12). The touching story of a unique friendship between an affectionate pig and the brilliant spider that lives above its pen.

Heidi by Johanna Spyri (ages 9-12). When her aunt tires of caring for her, orphaned Heidi is forced to live in the Alps with her gruff grandfather who comes to adore her.

*Be aware that some titles may contain evolutionary content   158

My Artiodactyl Project
Lesson 9

What I did:

What I learned:

FASCINATING FACTS

ABOUT
Lesson 10

SQUAMATES

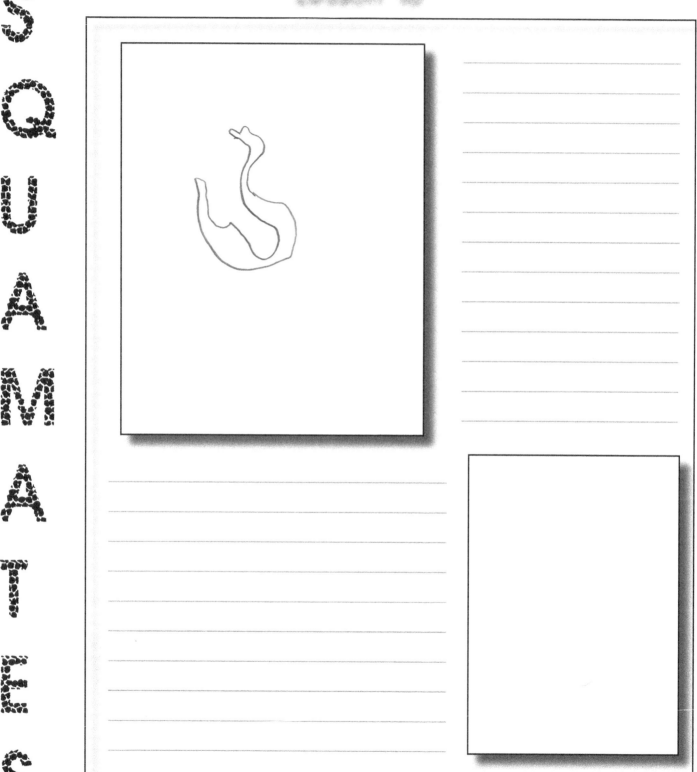

FASCINATING FACTS

ABOUT

Lesson 10

SQUAMATES

FASCINATING FACTS

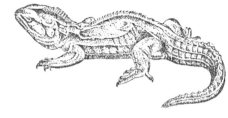

ABOUT
Lesson 10

TUATARAS

Name _____ Date _____

What Do You Remember?
Lesson 10 Review Questions

1. What do all reptiles have in common?

2. What kinds of animals are in order Squamata?

3. Why don't snakes blink?

4. How are their eyes protected?

5. How do snakes consume their prey?

6. What tooth does a reptile lose after its first molt?

7. Why don't you find molted lizard skins, even though you can find molted snake skins?

8. What is unique about gecko feet?

9. What is the difference between a tuatara and a lizard?

10. If a legless lizard looks like a worm, why isn't it considered a worm?

11. How do tuataras give us evidence for the Flood as described in the Bible?

LIZARDS

SNAKES

Special Snake Abilities

Lizards

Tuatara Speech

Lesson 10

Venomous Snakes in My Area
Lesson 10

Just as Moses lifted up the snake in the desert, so the Son of Man must be lifted up, that everyone who believes in him may have eternal life.

John 3:14-15

Just as Moses lifted up
the snake in the desert, so
the Son of Man must be
lifted up, that everyone who
believes in him may have
eternal life.

John 3:14-15

Vocabulary Crossword
Lesson 10

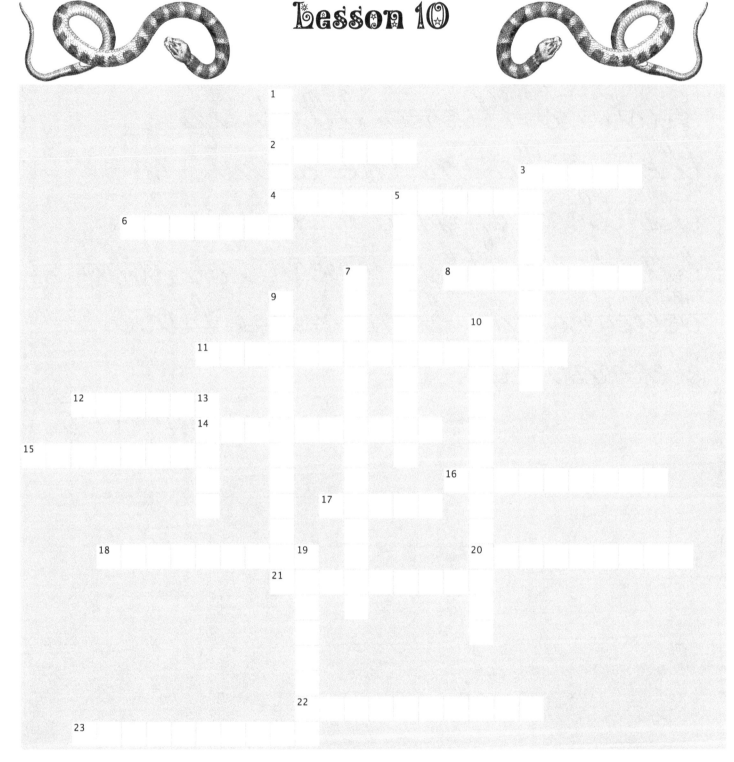

HERPS
SQUAMATA
RHYNCHOCEPHALIA
HEMOTOXIN
CONSTRICTORS
SCUTES
ANACONDAS
ELAPIDS

REPTILIA
TESTUDINES
SQUAMATES
JACOBSON'S ORGAN
COBRA
RATTLESNAKE
PYTHON
COLUBRIDS

ECTOTHERMIC
CROCODILIA
NEUROTOXIN
PIT VIPERS
EGG TOOTH
WATER MOCCASIN
VIPERS
SNAKE

Vocabulary Crossword
Lesson 10

Across

2. This species currently has the longest known snake in the world. It was found in Indonesia and was 33 feet long.
3. A term used to refer to both reptiles and amphibians.
4. A venomous snake that has modified scales on the end of its tail that bang against each other when it shakes its tail, making a rattling sound.
6. This group of snakes includes sea snakes. They are similar to vipers, but their venom is more powerful, and they are much more aggressive.
8. What a snake hatchling uses to tear open the shell so it can get out of the egg when ready. TWO WORDS
11. The tuatara is in this order.
12. Special scales on a snake's belly.
14. What we call snake venom that makes the muscles (including those that control breathing) stop working.
15. This class's name means "to creep." It contains lizards, turtles, snakes and the like.
16. These are sometimes called "typical snakes." They are generally venomless and many kill their prey by constriction.
17. When threatened, this type of snake tries to make itself look bigger by raising up and stretching out its hood.
18. These snakes have special sensory organs that enable them to sense heat. TWO WORDS
20. When length and weight are both considered, these snakes are the largest in the world.
21. A term used to refer to lizards and snakes.
22. This order contains turtles and tortoises.
23. Alligators and crocodiles are in this order.

Down

1. These snakes have long, hollow fangs used to inject venom into their prey. They fold their fangs away when they are not in use.
3. What we call snake venom that interferes with an animal's blood flow.
5. What we call animals that are cold-blooded.
7. An organ on the roof of the snake's mouth. It collects particles from the environment and tells the snake what's out there. TWO WORDS
9. These snakes coil their bodies around their prey, causing them to die from suffocation.
10. Another name for the cottonmouth. It is the only poisonous water snake. TWO WORDS
13. The most unlikeable kind of squamate.
19. The order of reptiles containing lizards and snakes.

Vocabulary Crossword
Lesson 10

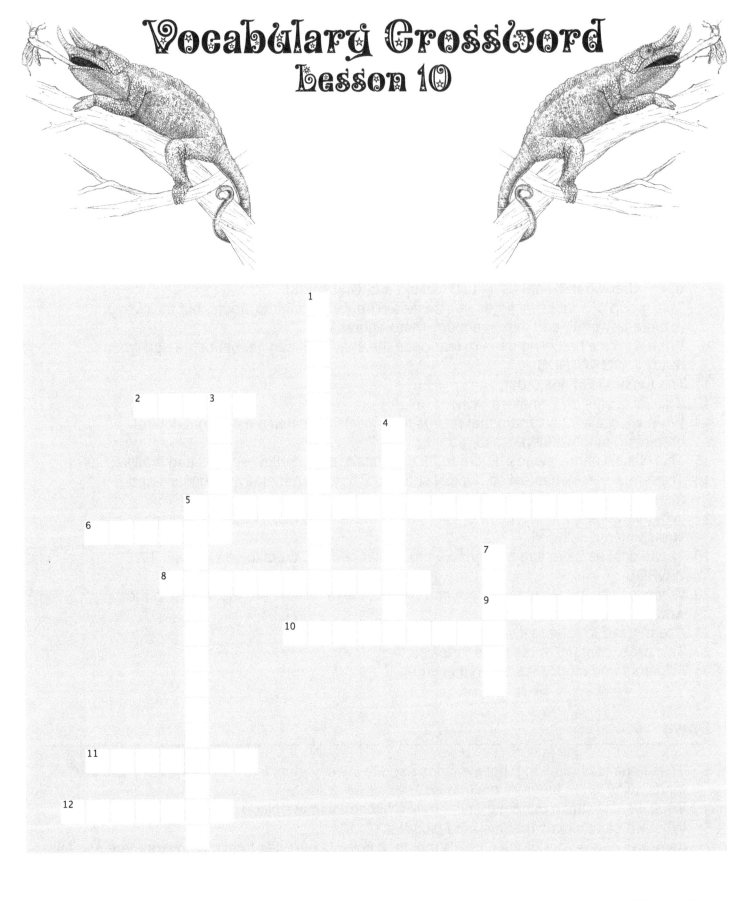

GILA MONSTER
IGUANAS
GECKOS
MONITOR LIZARDS
PINEAL EYE

MEXICAN BEADED LIZARD
CHAMELEON
SETAE
KOMODO DRAGON

LIZARDS
ANOLES
SKINKS
TUATARA

Vocabulary Crossword
Lesson 10

Across

2. Hair-like projections on a gecko's toes that stick to molecules on surfaces, enabling the gecko to climb up incredibly smooth surfaces, like glass.
5. A venomous lizard found in Mexico. THREE WORDS
6. Known as "chit-chat lizards" these animals talk, using chirping sounds to interact with each other.
8. A venomous New World lizard that is found in the deserts and scrubs of the southwestern United States. It rarely uses its venom for hunting. TWO WORDS
9. These squamates are popular pets. They can be found in tropical areas, and many types can change colors.
10. This creature has four layers of skin that help it accomplish its color changes.
11. This reptile's fossils have been found alongside dinosaur fossils. Its name means "spine bearer," and it can live to be 100 years old. It has only been able to survive in New Zealand and is in danger of becoming extinct.
12. There are many different types of these squamates with legs. They have a wide variety of tongues and scales and many have tails that can break off and grow back.

Down

1. This Indonesian monitor can grow longer than 9 feet, making it the longest lizard in creation. TWO WORDS
3. These common New World lizards can be vocal, crying out with squeals when stressed. Most males have a brightly colored flap of skin under the throat.
4. The third eye on some reptiles. It is located on top of the head between the two normal eyes and is used by tuataras to distinguish light from dark. TWO WORDS
5. These large, creeping animals have long necks with a narrow head and a pointed snout. They have a forked tongue and tend to swallow their prey whole.
7. Snake-like squamates with long, flat bodies, a long tail and a small pointy head. They can be found all over the world, except Antarctica.

Squamates Minibooks
Lesson 10

Paste your Squamates Pop Up
Books onto this page.

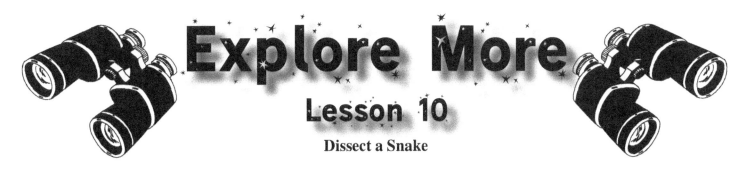

Explore More
Lesson 10
Dissect a Snake

Although some might find it objectionable to dissect animals, dissection is a great way to learn animal anatomy and physiology. When you purchase a specimen to dissect, you will also need to get an instruction manual and the supplies for the dissection. You can purchase preserved specimens from the following science supply companies: www.hometrainingtools.com, www.nilesbio.com, www.carolina.com, www.wardsci.com.

Science Fair Fun

Develop a science fair project based on a question you might have about snakes. For example, you might choose something from the following or make one up of your own: Are people more afraid of snakes or mice? Are people more afraid of snakes or spiders?

Decide what you believe and formulate some ideas for testing your belief.

Here's a good resource to help you create a science fair project step by step: *Strategies for Winning Science Fair Projects* by Joyce Henderson and Heather Tomasello.

Shed Your Skin!

This little game will have you and your friends competing to see who can shed their "skin" the fastest. You'll need some panty hose and some friends to begin! Since snakes do not have arms or hands, they have to rub up against things in nature, such as rocks, to get the skin off themselves. You can try it too! Put your hand into a panty hose and pull it up your arm. The hose is your skin. Have your friends put on their skin too. Now, yell "Go!" and have everyone try to get the "skin" off their arm without using their other hand or teeth. Try rubbing the hose on things in order to help get the skin off. The first person to get their skin all the way off wins!

DVD and Book Suggestion

Nature: Reptiles, Snakes and Lizards (1982) distributed by PBS. Offers viewers a close and personal look at these fascinating and yet often deadly creatures.
Crinkleroot's Visit to Crinkle Cove by Jim Arnosky (ages 3-6). In this colorful picture book, Crinkleroot searches for his friend (a small orange snake) from the woods to the lake, examining the animals and plants he encounters along the way.
Snakes Are Hunters by Patricia Lauber (ages 3-6). A colorful and basic introduction for very young children to the world of snakes.
All About Lizards by Jim Arnosky (ages 4-8). A picture book that introduces young children to the world of lizards, answering questions about characteristics, habitats, and behaviors.
All About Rattlesnakes by Jim Arnosky (ages 4-8). Examines the different kinds of rattlesnakes and their unique characteristics, life cycles, habitats, behaviors, and more.
Chameleons by Jake Miller (ages 4-8). A picture book that describes the life cycle, habitat, and behavior of chameleons.
Komodo! by Peter Sis (ages 4-8). A young boy who loves dragons travels with his parents to the Indonesian island of Komodo in hopes of seeing a real dragon.
A Snake in the House by Faith McNulty (ages 4-8). An escaped snake finds many clever places to hide throughout a house, while the boy who brought him home searches for him.
Rikki-Tikki-Tavi, contained in The Jungle Book by Rudyard Kipling (ages 6+). A gripping adventure about a mongoose that kills a pair of cobras and saves a family.
Akimbo and the Snakes by Alexander McCall Smith (ages 6-9). On a trip to a snake park with his Uncle Peter, Akimbo has an adventure involving a deadly green mamba snake.
A Water Snake's Year by Doris Gove (ages 6-9). A picture book follows a year in the life of a female water snake.
Alice and the Boa Constrictor by Laurie Adams (ages 9-12). After learning in science class that boa constrictors make wonderful pets, Alice saves her money until she has enough to buy one of her very own.
Day of the Iguana by Henry Winkler (ages 9-12). Hank was never fond of his sister's pet iguana, and the relationship worsens when it lays its eggs inside his science project.

*Be aware that some titles may contain evolutionary content   175

My Squamate Project

Lesson 10

What I did:

What I learned:

FASCINATING FACTS

ABOUT

REPTILES

AND

AMPHIBIANS

LESSON 11

What Do You Remember?
Lesson 11 Review Questions

1. What are the differences among turtles, terrapins, and tortoises?

2. Can snapping turtles pull their heads into their shells?

3. How do they protect themselves?

4. How does the alligator snapping turtle catch prey?

5. What is interesting about the snake-necked turtles of South America and Australia?

6. Explain the differences among the different kinds of crocodilians.

7. How do crocodilians care for their young?

8. Explain the stages in an amphibian's life.

9. What is the main difference between a salamander and a newt?

Reptiles   Amphibians

TESTUDINES
LESSON 11

AMPHIBIANS
LESSON 11

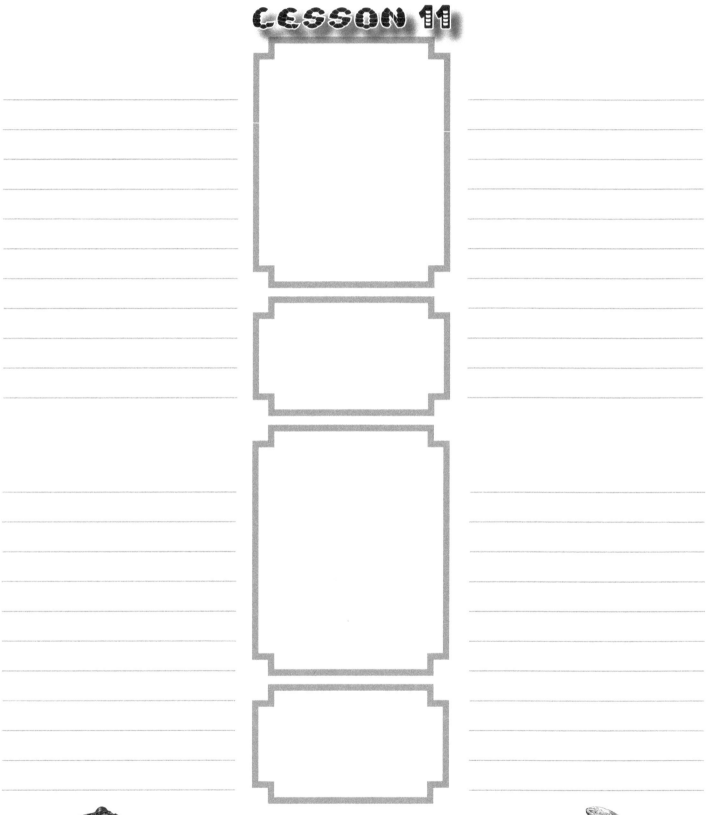

LIFE OF AMPHIBIAN DIARY

LESSON 11

So Aaron stretched out his hand over the waters of Egypt, and the frogs came up and covered the land.

Exodus 8:6

So Aaron stretched out his hand over the waters of Egypt, and the frogs came up and covered the land.

Exodus 8:6

Vocabulary Crossword
Lesson 11

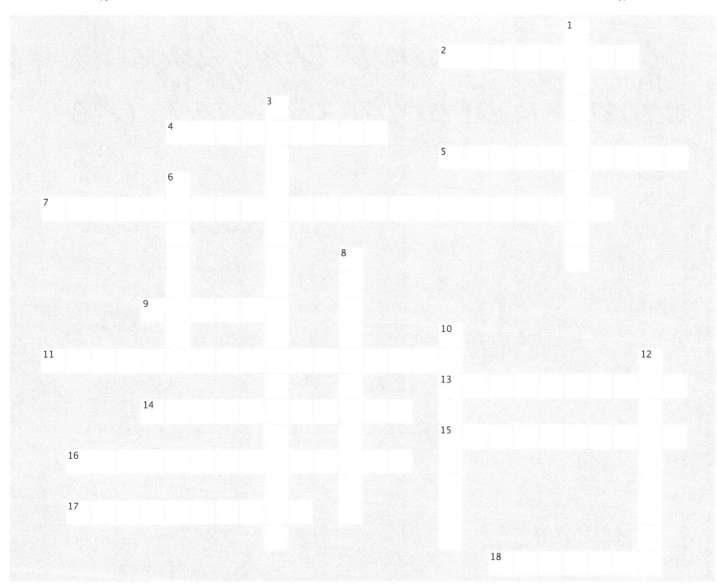

TESTUDINES
TORTOISES
CAIMANS
MUSK TURTLES
CROCODILIA
ALLIGATORS

CARAPACE
TERRAPINS
SOFT-SHELLED TURTLES
MUD TURTLES
SIDE-NECKED TURTLES
GASTROLITHS

PLASTRON
PIG-NOSED TURTLE
ESTUARIES
ALLIGATOR SNAPPING TURTLE
CROCODILES
GAVIAL

Vocabulary Crossword
Lesson 11

Across

2. The bottom part of a turtle's shell.
4. These turtles do not have webbed feet, living mostly on dry land. The largest can grow to be more than 4 feet long.
5. Large reptiles make up the members of this order, including alligators and crocodiles.
7. This snapper can reach weights of greater than 200 pounds. It has a horny shell and catches its prey by wiggling its bright pink tongue under the water. THREE WORDS
9. This reptile can be distinguished by its very long snout with a bump on the end.
11. Turtles that don't tuck their head in straight back, but instead turn it to the side to hide it under their shell. THREE WORDS
13. Turtles belong in this order.
14. These turtles release an offensive odor when bothered. TWO WORDS
15. These large reptiles have a U-shaped snout with only a few teeth from the upper jaw showing when their mouth is closed. They also have a bone that separates the two nostrils in the nose.
16. This freshwater turtle has flippers and looks like a sea turtle with a piglike nose. It comes to land to lay its eggs and swims in ponds, lakes and streams in northern Australia and southern New Guinea. THREE WORDS
17. Grouped in the same family as musk turtles, these carnivorous creatures eat vegetation from time to time. TWO WORDS
18. These reptiles have a lot more bony plates protecting their underside than do alligators. They are nocturnal, and their size varies greatly among the species, from 5 inches to 12 feet.

Down

1. These reptiles have a V-shaped snout, and many of their teeth show when their mouth is closed.
3. These turtles' shells are soft, thin and flat, and they burrow just beneath the mud at the bottom of a lake or pond. They have an unusually long neck and a long snorkel-like nose. THREE WORDS
6. The top part of a turtle's shell.
8. Stones that are stored in the stomach and grind up the food once it has been swallowed.
10. Areas where a river meets an ocean. The waters are salty, but not quite as salty as the ocean.
12. These turtles spend a lot of time both on dry land and in water.

Vocabulary Crossword
Lesson 11

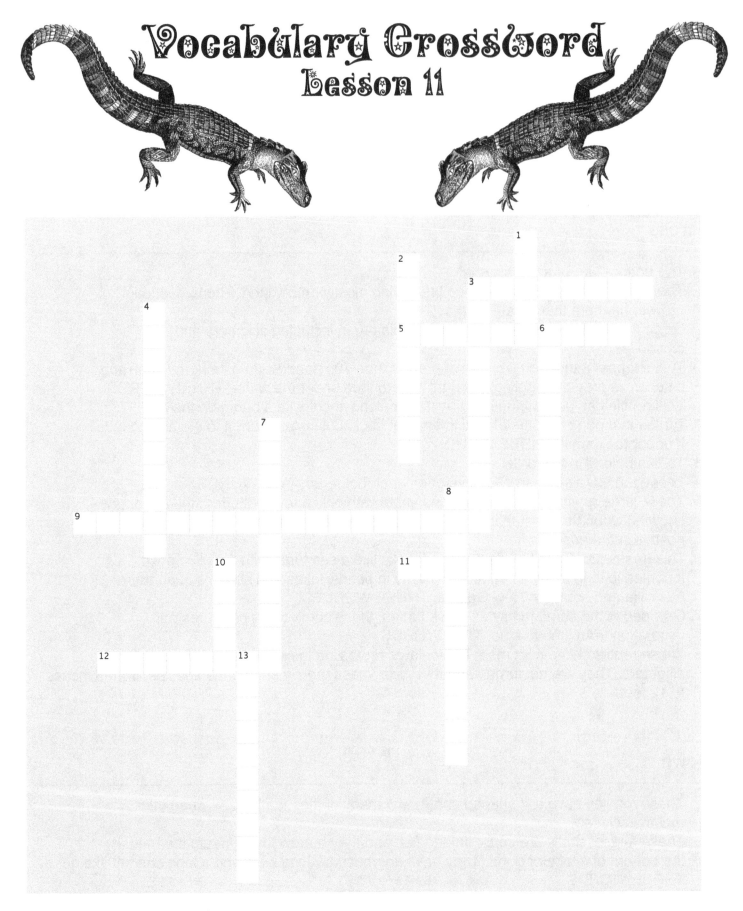

AMPHIBIANS	SPAWNING	EGG STAGE
TADPOLE STAGE	METAMORPH	FROGLET STAGE
ADULT STAGE	FROGS	TOADS
VOCAL SAC	NEWTS	SALAMANDERS
AQUATIC SALAMANDERS	SEMI-AQUATIC	TERRESTRIAL

Vocabulary Crossword
Lesson 11

Across

3. The stage of the frog's life when eggs are laid.
5. When the frog has completed its cycle. This stage happens around four months of age. TWO WORDS
8. These amphibians have smooth, wet skin and must live in or very near water.
9. Salamanders that stay in the water almost all the time. TWO WORDS
11. The stage in a frog's life when it is in the egg.
12. The place where the male Darwin's frog keeps its young while they develop. TWO WORDS

Down

1. These creatures have bumpy, thick skin and can travel across dry land for quite some time before they dry out.
2. The stage in a frog's life when hind legs start to sprout and the gills begin to be replaced by lungs is called the _____ stage.
3. These amphibians look like slimy lizards. They have tails and long, slender bodies.
4. Salamanders and newts that spend most of their adult life on land, returning to the water only to mate are called _____ salamanders.
6. The stage in a frog's life when it breathes with gills, like a fish. TWO WORDS
7. What we call salamanders that spend some of their time as adults in water and some on land.
8. The stage in a frog's life when it has a tail. TWO WORDS
10. These salamanders have rougher skin that is more like that of a toad's.
13. The name of these animals means "dual life." They begin like a fish in the water and later develop legs and lungs to live on land.

HERPS MINIBOOKS
LESSON 11

Paste your Herps Pop Up Books
onto this page.

Explore More
Lesson 11

Make a Paper Mache Turtle

You can create your own paper mache turtle starting with a balloon! It will take a few days to finish, but you'll have lots of fun making your turtle.

You will need:

Some newspaper (cut into strips)
Paste (half white flour and half warm water)
A piece of cardboard
Acrylic paint (shades of green, white, black, red)
Scissors
A medium-sized bowl
Masking tape
A paintbrush
A paper plate
Varnish

First, blow up your balloon and tie it securely. Mix the flour and water to create your paste. Dip the paper strips in the paste and lay them on the surface of the balloon until it is completely covered. Allow your balloon to dry overnight. Next, crumple a piece of newspaper into a walnut-sized ball. Now wrap another piece of newspaper around the ball and gather the ends to make the turtle's head and neck. Cover it with strips of newspaper dipped in the paste. Cover the balloon with another layer of pasty strips. Let everything dry completely. Next, cut the balloon (the turtle's shell) in half. Cut out of the cardboard a tail and four feet. Attach them to the bottom of the shell with masking tape. Now, cut an opening in the front of the shell and stick in the turtle's neck. Tape it in place. Cover everything with one more layer of strips and paste, being sure to securely attach the turtle's feet, neck and tail. Let your turtle dry completely for one or two days.

Now it's time to paint your turtle! You can make it look realistic or give it a bright, creative design. Once the paint has dried, apply a coat of varnish over your turtle for a finished look.

Lily Pad Leap Frog

Have you ever played leap frog? Well in this version, the frogs do the leaping! Fill a child's plastic pool with water. Cut 10 lily pads out of craft foam. Now, find 20 plastic frogs that are small enough and light enough to sit on top of the floating pads. Number the lily pads (one to ten) with a waterproof marker and place them in the pool. Have two people begin tossing frogs on the pads trying to get a frog to land on each of the lily pads, in numerical order. The person who gets a frog to leap on all the lily pads wins!

Fly Toss!

This is a fun and tasty game for you and your friends. You are going to pretend to be frogs catching flies! To begin, have you and some friends divide into pairs. Stand in two rows, facing your partner about three feet apart. One partner is the frog and the other is the fly. When an adult says, "Go!" the fly begins tossing raisins (flies) into the frog's mouth. The frog must catch the flies on his tongue for the catch to count. Once the frog has successfully caught five flies, the partners switch places and begin tossing again. Have an adult let you know when three minutes are up. The partners who tossed and caught the most flies win!

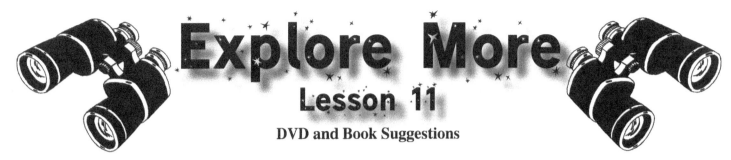

Explore More
Lesson 11
DVD and Book Suggestions

Nature: Reptiles (1982) distributed by PBS. Examines the worlds of alligators, crocodiles, turtles and tortoises.

All About Alligators by Jim Arnosky (ages 4-8). A picture book that describes the physical characteristics, behaviors, and survival techniques of different kinds of alligators.

All About Frogs by Jim Arnosky (ages 4-8). A picture book introduction to the physical characteristics, habitats, and behaviors of frogs.

All About Turtles by Jim Arnosky (ages 4-8). A picture book that describes the physical characteristics, behavior, and survival techniques of different kinds of land and sea turtles.

Alligators and Crocodiles by Gail Gibbons (ages 4-8). A picture book introduction to the physical characteristics, habitats, and behaviors of alligators and crocodiles.

Big Night for Salamanders by Sarah Lamstein (ages 4-8). A boy and his parents go out on a rainy night in spring to help salamanders cross a busy road on their annual migration to the vernal pools in which they breed.

Box Turtle at Long Pond by William T. George (ages 4-8). A day in the life of a box turtle is chronicled with realistic illustrations and clear text.

A Crocodile Grows Up by Amanda Doering Tourville (ages 4-8). Follows the life of a Nile crocodile as it grows to adulthood.

Fantastic Frogs by Fay Robinson (ages 4-8). Colorful illustration and verse introduce young children to the life cycle, habits and habitats of frogs.

Frogs by Gail Gibbons (ages 4-8). A picture book introduction to the characteristics, habitats, life cycle and behaviors of frogs.

Hip Pocket Papa by Sandra Markle (ages 4-8). Watercolor illustrations follow one Australian hip-pocket frog as it guards the eggs and subsequent tadpoles that emerge and climb into the fantastic hidden pockets of its legs.

A Mama for Owen by Marion Dane Bauer (ages 4-8). A picture book based on the true story of a baby hippopotamus who, separated from its mother during the Indian Ocean Tsunami of 2004, bonds with a giant tortoise.

One Tiny Turtle by Nicola Davies (ages 4-8). A picture book containing lyrical text that follows the mysterious life of a loggerhead turtle as it is born, grows, journeys, and returns to shore to start a new cycle of life.

The Salamander Room by Anne Mazer (ages 4-8). A young boy finds a salamander and considers, with his mother's help, how to make a proper home for it, realizing its natural habitat is best.

Spoonbill Swamp by Brenda Z. Guiberson (ages 4-8). Realistic illustrations and an engaging plot depict one day in the life of an alligator and the spoonbill that shares its swamp habitat.

Toad by the Road: A Year in the Life of These Amazing Amphibians by Joanne Ryder (ages 4-8). Poems and illustrations trace the yearly life cycle of toads, from spring tadpoles to adults hibernating in the winter.

Turtle Summer: A Journal for My Daughter by Mary Alice Monroe (ages 4-8). A mother's journal of a summer spent with her daughter on an island among loggerhead turtles.

Let's Get Turtles! by Millicent Salsam (ages 6-9). Two boys who really wanted turtles for pets learn to take care of them at home.

The Moon of the Alligators by Jean Craighead George (ages 6-9). Describes an alligator's search for food in the drying rivers of the Florida Everglades during the month of October.

The Moon of the Salamander by Jean Craighead George (age 6-9). On the night of the first spring rain, a male salamander journeys to a breeding pond, encountering various plants and animals that share his habitat.

Red Spotted Newt by Doris Gove (ages 6-9). Through realistic watercolor illustrations and clear, informative text, this book follows a year in the life of a newt as it searches for food, escapes predators, mates and returns to lay its own eggs.

Owen and Mzee: The True Story of a Remarkable Friendship by Isabella Hatkoff (ages 7-10). The true story of a baby hippopotamus who, separated from its mother during the Indian Ocean Tsunami of 2004, bonds with a giant tortoise.

Owen and Mzee: The Language of Friendship by Isabella Hatkoff (ages 7-10). Continues the story of the unique friendship between an orphaned hippo and a 130-year-old tortoise.

Mike's Toads by Wilson Gage (ages 9-12). A sixth-grade boy volunteers his brother's services once too often without consulting him and ends up having to spend his summer vacation caring for a friend's toads.

Minn of the Mississippi by Holling C. Holling (ages 9-12) Newberry Honor Book. Follow the adventures of Minn, a three-legged snapping turtle, as she slowly makes her way from her birthplace at the headwaters of the Mississippi River to the Gulf of Mexico.

The Wind in the Willows by Kenneth Grahame (ages 9-12). The classic and enchanting adventures of Mole, Water Rat, Badger, and Toad.

*Be aware that some titles may contain evolutionary content   192

My Herps Project
Lesson 11

What I did:

What I learned:

FASCINATING FACTS

ABOUT

DINOSAURS

LESSON 12

the name dinosaurs was reclently called in 1841 We have found severale fossils we don't get all the information from fossils they can't get all the

information but a draling helps

FASCINATING FACTS

ABOUT DINOSAURS

LESSON 12

What Do You Remember?
Lesson 12 Review Questions

1. What evidence do we have that dinosaurs lived during the same time as people?

some people q flexible tissue which had
blood which was t n o m
afew thousand

2. What's the difference between dinosaurs and other reptiles?

3. What are the two main groups of dinosaurs?

4. What are some special features of sauropods?

5. Which animal does Behemoth best describe and why?

6. What are some special features of theropods?

7. In which group of dinosaurs is *Stegosaurus* placed?

8. In which group are the duck-billed dinosaurs placed?

9. What are some possible reasons for the extinction of dinosaurs?

SAUROPODS
LESSON 12

THEROPODS
LESSON 12

THYREOPHORA

MARGINOCEPHALIA
LESSON 12

ORNITHOPODA

"Look at the behemoth, which I made along with you and which feeds on grass like an ox. What strength he has in his loins, what power in the muscles of his belly! His tail sways like a cedar; the sinews of his thighs are close-knit."

Job 40:15-17

"Look at the behemoth, which I made along with you and which feeds on grass like an ox. What strength he has in his loins, what Power in the muscles of his belly! His tail sways like a cedar; the sinews of his thighs are close-knit.

"Look at the behemoth, which I made along with you and which feeds on grass like an ox. What strength he has in his loins, what power in the muscles of his belly! His tail sways like a cedar; the sinews of his thighs are close-knit."

Job 40:15-17

Vocabulary Crossword
Lesson 12

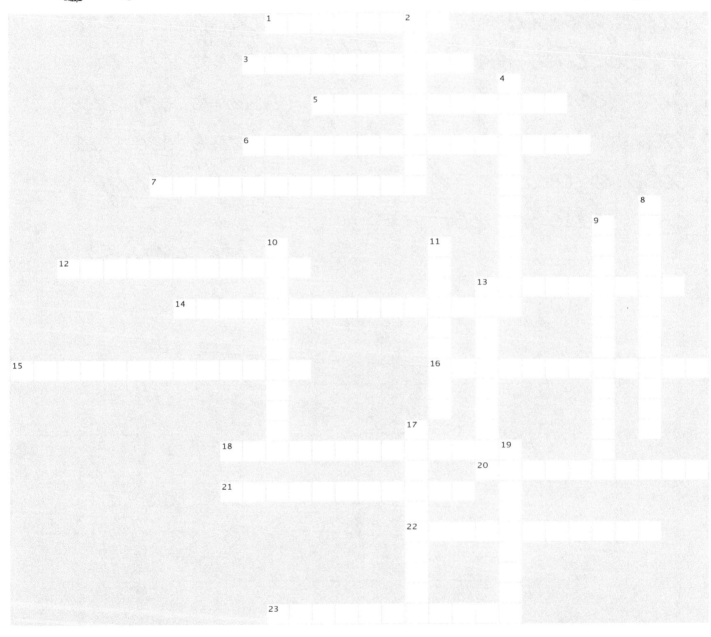

DINOSAURS
PALEONTOLOGISTS
THEROPODS
CAMARASAURUS
SPINOSAURUS
ANKYLOSAURUS
HADROSAURS
HYPSILOPHODON

BEHEMOTH
SAURISCHIA
BRACHIOSAURUS
CETIOSAURUS
CERATOSAURS
THYREOPHORA
MARGINOCEPHALIA
CHEEK TEETH

SAUROPODS
ORNITHISCHIA
DIPLODOCUS
TYRANNOSAURUS
DROMAEOSAURS
STEGOSAURUS
ORNITHOPODA
IGUANODON

Vocabulary Crossword
Lesson 12

Across

1. A description of this sauropod-like animal can be found in the book of Job in the Bible.
3. Teeth in the back of a dinosaur's mouth. TWO WORDS
5. This genus contains species of theropods with large spines on their back. The fossils of this genus have been found in northern Africa.
6. Scientists who study fossils.
7. This dinosaur's name means "fused lizard," because the plates on its back seem fused together. It also had a club at the end of the tail that was most likely used for defense.
12. The knights of the dinosaur world, with armor protecting their slow and steady frame.
13. The name of these extinct creatures means "terrible lizard."
14. The dinosaurs with margins on their heads.
15. Meaning "high-crested tooth," this dinosaur had a horned beak, cheek pouches and a mouth full of cheek teeth.
16. "Swift-running lizards." These theropods had stiff tails, claws on the feet and hands, and one retractable, sickle-shaped claw on each foot.
18. The animals in this sauropod genus had front legs that were longer than their back legs.
20. "Lizard-hipped" dinosaurs.
21. Meaning "whale lizard," this genus got its name from fossils that were thought to have come from a large sea-living reptile.
22. This dinosaur had plates on its back and 2-foot long spikes on its tail. Its name means "covered lizard."
23. A large group of theropods that gets their name from a small horn on their snout. Paleontologists believe they were social animals as their fossils are often found in groups.

Down

2. These "beast-footed" dinosaurs were carnivores that walked on two legs. Fossils of these creatures are extremely rare.
4. "Bird-hipped" dinosaurs.
8. This genus name means "chambered lizard."
9. This genus, whose name means "tyrant lizard," contains the well-known species T-rex.
10. These bird-footed dinosaurs were mostly bipedal with three toes.
11. The name of a genus whose dinosaurs had teeth that strongly resemble those of an iguana.
13. The dinosaurs in this sauropod genus had front legs that were shorter than their back legs, giving them a more horizontal posture.
17. These dinosaurs had an elongated face that ended in a broad, flattened snout, resembling the bill of a duck.
19. A group of herbivorous dinosaurs thought to have spent a lot of time in the water. Their fossils have been found in Antarctica.

DINOS MINIBOOKS
LESSON 12

Paste your Dinosaur String Tie
Books onto this page.

Explore More
Lesson 12

Create a Dinosaur Diorama

With careful planning, you can create an amazing dinosaur diorama to display. This will probably take a few days, but take your time and have fun! You can purchase dinosaur tubes or dinosaur figurines from craft stores. If you can find figurines of people, you should also include them in your diorama. You will need things like paint, paper, clay, glue and materials from outside, such as moss, sticks, or stones. You can use newspaper covered with a mixture of water and flour to make a mountain (paper mache). It is a good idea to create your diorama on a large piece of cardboard or inside a large box (turned sideways).

Plan or draw out what you want your dinosaur diorama to look like. Then begin by creating the foundation and base of the structure. Next, paint your foundation before adding the natural materials. Finally, add the dinosaurs and people!

Dinosaur Spelling Bee

You can turn learning those long dinosaur names into fun with your friends if you have a dinosaur spelling bee! Copy all the dinosaur names from the lesson onto index cards. Have some friends do the same. Give yourselves a week to study the names and set a date for the bee. It might be fun to choose an evening when the all the families can come watch. Remember, the purpose is to learn so keep the competition friendly. Finish the evening with a special dinosaur-related treat to celebrate learning to spell all those tricky names!

DVD and Book Suggestions

Dinosaurs, Genesis, and the Gospel by Ken Ham and Buddy Davis (ages 5-11). Music and more teach the days of creation, including the animals God made—especially dinosaurs!
The Riddle of the Dinosaurs by Mike Riddle (Answers in Genesis resource, ages 5-11). Through animation, this book provides answers to questions kids have about dinosaurs.
Dinosaurs in the Bible? by Ken Ham (ages 12+). Teaches older students and adults about dinosaurs from a biblical perspective.
D is for Dinosaur by Ken & Mally Ham (ages 2-11). Whimsical illustrations and simple verse bring the gospel message to young children.
Dinosaurs for Kids by Ken Ham (ages 5-11). Dramatic illustrations accompany a bevy of information about dinosaurs, including names, what the Bible has to say about them, and dinosaur fossil evidence.
Dinosaurs: Stars of the Show by Amy Zordel (ages 5-11). A Saturday-morning television program about dinosaurs boasts "millions of years," creating an opportunity for one young viewer to stand up and proudly showcase her faith in the Bible.
Dinosaurs in Eden by Ken Ham (ages 8+). Travel back in time to the Garden of Eden, a real world created by God and inhabited by dinosaurs.
Dinosaurs, the Lost World, and You by Dr. John Norris (ages 8+). Colorfully illustrated text answers the questions, "From where did dinosaurs come?" and "Where are they now?"
Dinosaurs by Design by Ken Ham (ages 8-11). Everything you want to know about dinosaurs and how they relate to the Bible.
The Great Dinosaur Mystery and the Bible by Paul S. Taylor (ages 8-11). Explains how dinosaurs are a part of God's creation and uses them to introduce a host of biblical concepts.
What Really Happened to the Dinosaurs? by Dr. John Morris and Ken Ham (ages 8-11). Colorful illustrations take children on a journey back in time to provide an answer to this common question.
Creation Sensation Dinosaur Adventure by Steve and Carla Hardwick. An excellent collection of some of the best creation-based books and videos about dinosaurs that are available on the market today. In addition, the kit also includes authentic dinosaur fossils and museum quality replicas, crafts, hands-on activities, and a guidebook to help you traverse through a maze of false information to discover the truth about dinosaurs and the Bible. Great for family nights, homeschool co-ops, and church or youth groups!

*Be aware that some titles may contain evolutionary content

My Dino Project

Lesson 12

What I did:

What I learned:

Scientific Speculation Sheet

Dinosaur and Lizard Models

Lesson 12

Name_____ Date _____

Materials Used:

Procedure:

Hypothesis:

Results:

Conclusion:

FASCINATING FACTS
ABOUT
Arthropods
Lesson 13

Spider Webs
Lesson 13

What Do You Remember?
Lesson 13 Review Questions

1. How can you identify an arthropod?

2. How can you tell the difference between an insect and an arachnid?

3. What are the two most dangerous spiders in the United States?

4. How do spiders consume their prey?

5. Name some of the things spiders do with their silk.

6. From where does the silk come?

7. What are some of the different kinds of webs that spiders build?

8. What are some ways spiders capture their prey?

9. What are harvestmen?

10. How do they defend themselves?

11. Why are harvestmen good for your garden?

12. What animals eat scorpions?

13. What are acarina?

14. Name some specific kinds of acarina?

15. Why are ticks dangerous?

16. Name some differences between centipedes and millipedes.

17. Where do wood lice live?

18. How do they defend themselves?

ARTHROPODS UP CLOSE
Lesson 13

INTERESTING ARTHROPODS
Lesson 13

INTERESTING ARTHROPODS
Lesson 13

"Which of you fathers, if your son asks for a fish, will give him a snake instead? Or if he asks for an egg, will give him a scorpion?"
Luke 11:11-12

"Which of you fathers, if your son asks for a fish, will give him a snake instead? Or if he asks for an egg, will give him a scorpion?"

Luke 11:11-12

Vocabulary Crossword
Lesson 13

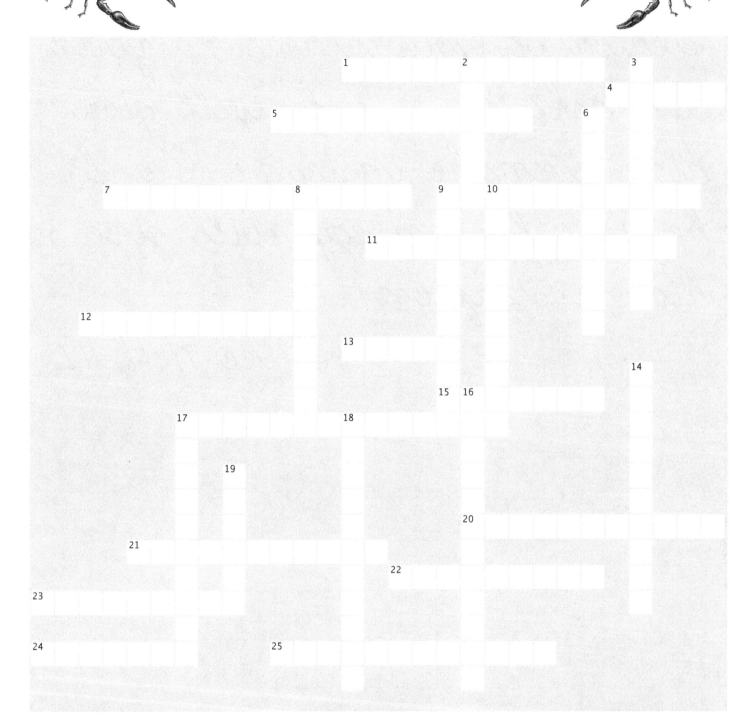

ARTHROPODS
SPIDER
FANGS
SETAE
BLACK WIDOW
EGG CASE SILK
RADIAL LINES
SHEET WEBS
TARANTULAS

INVERTEBRATES
PEDIPALPS
ABDOMEN
TARSUS
DRAGLINE SILK
SPIDERLINGS
FUNNEL WEBS
WOLF SPIDERS
FISHING SPIDERS

ARACHNIDS
CHELICERAE
CEPHALOTHORAX
BROWN RECLUSE
CAPTURE SILK
ORB WEBS
TANGLE WEBS
CRAB SPIDERS
HARVESTMEN

Vocabulary Crossword
Lesson 13

Across

1. The special water-proof silk the spider wraps around its eggs. TWO WORDS
4. Tiny "swords" on the end of an arachnid's chelicerae.
5. Silk used to catch prey in a spider's web. It is also used by those spiders that actually shoot out strands of silk to catch prey. TWO WORDS
7. The legs and pedipalps are attached to this part of an arachnid.
9. These spiders wait in ambush to pounce on their prey. Many are brightly colored, matching the flowers in which they hide. TWO WORDS
11. Creatures without a backbone.
12. These notoriously hairy spiders are often kept as pets. When threatened, they spew barbed hairs containing an irritating chemical onto the potential predator.
13. Hairs on a spider's legs that help it sense the outside world.
15. One of the two parts of an arachnid. It contains several organs, including the lungs.
17. These spiders can be found at the edge of the water and can actually run on the surface to catch an insect or small fish. TWO WORDS
20. The "rays" a spider makes, stretching across the entire web, spreading it out in several directions. TWO WORDS
21. Fast-moving hunters that track down their prey. They have three rows of eyes, and the young stay upon the mother's abdomen until after the first molt. TWO WORDS
22. These creatures have eight legs. Spiders, scorpions, ticks and mites are also in this group.
23. Flat web sheets that lay across vegetation or outdoor structures, looking like an acrobat's safety net. TWO WORDS
24. Webs that are composed of round elements. They are made of strands that form circles. TWO WORDS
25. The strongest silk a spider makes. The strands are like safety lines the spider uses to make a quick escape if danger approaches. TWO WORDS

Down

2. This eight-legged creature is equipped with many eyes and thousands of hairs on its legs.
3. Also called "cobwebs," these look like random masses of threads that sprawl out here and there. Black widows spin these types of webs. TWO WORDS
6. Sensitive appendages that give arachnids a good sense of touch and can be used for handling food as well as for defense.
8. Sometimes called "daddy longlegs" these eight-legged arachnids are not spiders.
9. Mouthparts on an arachnid that end in fangs.
10. These creatures are identified by their tough exoskeleton and segmented body. They do not have a backbone, and their name means "jointed foot."
14. This spider is shiny and black, and the female has a red, hourglass-shaped mark on the underside of its abdomen. Its venom is toxic and its bite very painful. TWO WORDS
16. Yellow to brown in color, this spider has a violin pattern on its cephalothorax. Its venom is highly poisonous and can produce a deep painful wound. TWO WORDS
17. Little webbed sinkholes in the ground. The spider waits at the bottom for the prey to fall in. TWO WORDS
18. What we call baby spiders.
19. A foot at the bottom of a spider's leg.

Vocabulary Crossword
Lesson 13

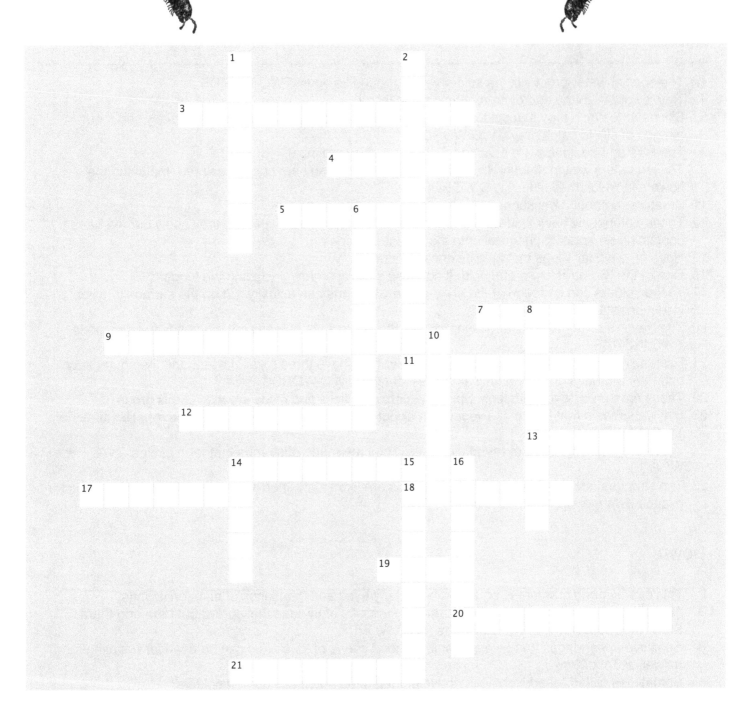

SCORPIONS
BARK SCORPION
ACARINA
MANGE
HOST
CENTIPEDE
MILLIPEDES
PEREON

METASOMA
WHIP SCORPIONS
SCABIES
DUST MITES
SOFT TICK
CHILOPODA
ISOPODS

TELSON
FALSE SCORPIONS
CHIGGERS
HARD TICK
TICKS
DIPLOPODA
WOODLOUSE

Vocabulary Crossword
Lesson 13

Across

3. A species of scorpion that lives in North America and can bring harm to people with its potent venom. TWO WORDS
4. The end of a scorpion's tail. It is sharp and has a venomous stinger used on predators and prey.
5. This little crustacean is the only one completely at home on land. It breathes through gill-like structures and must stay in moist environments.
7. These members of the acarina feed on blood and can transmit several kinds of diseases.
9. Also called "pseudoscorpions," these tiny creatures are smaller than an inch and can spin silk like spiders. They have pedipalps but no metasoma. TWO WORDS
11. These fearsome-looking creatures have lobster-like pedipalps used to capture and tear up prey.
12. The larvae of harvest mites.
13. The isopod's thorax.
14. These creatures have two feet on each side of each segment of their body. They have a tough exoskeleton and curl up to protect themselves from harm.
17. Tiny parasites known as mites and ticks. They can spread disease, decay and even death.
18. The wood louse is an example of these types of creatures.
19. What we call an animal or person a tick feeds on.
20. This long-bodied creature has between thirty and a few hundred feet. It is a carnivore and sports venomous fangs that kill its prey.
21. The scorpion's tail.

Down

1. A tick that feeds on its host for a long time, leaving its host when it needs to molt. Its mouthparts are visible. TWO WORDS
2. These arachnids have a "whip" for a tail and glands that emit foul-smelling chemicals. TWO WORDS
6. These tiny creatures feast on dead skin and can cause terrible allergies. TWO WORDS
8. The class to which centipedes belong.
10. A type of mite that burrows under the skin, causing an itchy patch.
14. A disease that a dog gets when it is attacked by mange mites, causing patches of skin to show through its coat.
15. Millipedes are members of this class.
16. A tick that feeds on its host for a short period of time. Its mouthparts are mostly hidden on the underside of its body. TWO WORDS

ARTHROPODS MINIBOOK
Lesson 13

Paste your Arthropods Fan onto
this page.

Explore More
Lesson 13

Make a Spider Craft

There are many different craft activities found on the Internet for constructing a spider. Choose one of them to do, or see if you can make a spider using items found outside in nature.

Stage a Spider Puppet Show

Make a spider and a scorpion out of socks. Then, write a play about a spider that meets a scorpion. Have them discuss their differences with one another. Try to make it both educational and entertaining. Create a stage for your puppet show and put a show on for your family and friends!

Lacy Spider Webs

You can create a spider web to hang in the kitchen window! Here's how: begin with a sheet of wax paper. Now, using thin lines of white glue, design a spider web on the wax paper. Sprinkle the web with glitter and let it dry completely. Next, carefully peel away the wax paper and stick your web creation in the window! You can add a small plastic spider if you'd like. You could also purchase colored glue for a more creative look.

Spaghetti Spider Webs

Create a spider web with cooked spaghetti and glue. Start with a bowl of cooked spaghetti. Now, pour in some white glue and mix the spaghetti with your hands. Next, pull individual strands of spaghetti out of the bowl and begin designing your web on a black piece of construction paper. Allow the web to dry completely. Carefully pull the web off the paper, if you'd like. You can tie a string to the top and hang it as a decoration. You can also divide your spaghetti into separate containers and use different colors of glue for a colorful web design.

Book Suggestions

A Very Busy Spider by Eric Carle (ages 3-6). With trademark colorful illustrations and simple text, witness a day in the life of a very busy spider.
The Lady and the Spider by Faith McNulty (ages 4-8). A lady finds a spider in a head of lettuce and releases it back into her garden.
Once I Knew a Spider by Jennifer Dewey (ages 4-8). A woman expecting her first child watches as an orb weaver spider spins a web, lays eggs, and stays with them over the winter.
Spectacular Spiders by Linda Glasser (ages 4-8). Sneak a colorful peek into a day in the life of a garden spider as seen through the eyes of a young girl.
Spiders by Gail Gibbons (ages 4-8). A picture book that examines the physical characteristics, behaviors, and habitats of different kinds of spiders.
Spinning Spiders by Melvin Berger (ages 4-8). A picture book that describes the characteristics of spiders and the methods they use to trap their prey in webs.
Discovering Centipedes and Millipedes by Ken Preston-Mafham (ages 6-9). Examines the physical characteristics, feeding, reproduction, defenses, and other activities of centipedes and millipedes.
Like Jake and Me by Mavis Jukes (ages 9-12) Newberry Honor Book. Alex feels he does not have much in common with his stepfather Jake until a fuzzy spider brings them together.
Scorpion Man: Exploring the World of Scorpions by Laurence P. Pringle (ages 9-12). A photographic account of the work of a wildlife biologist who specializes in scorpions.
The Life of a Spider by Jean-Henri Fabre (ages 12+). A substantial text by a renowned naturalist compiles over fifty years of observations, study and experiments for those children with a desire to know all they can about the life of a spider.

*Be aware that some titles may contain evolutionary content   221

My Arthropod Project

Lesson 13

What I did:

What I learned:

Scientific Speculation Sheet

Wood Louse Population

Lesson 13

Name_____   Date _____

Materials Used:

Procedure:

Hypothesis:

Results:

Conclusion:

FASCINATING FACTS
ABOUT
GASTROPODS
LESSON 14

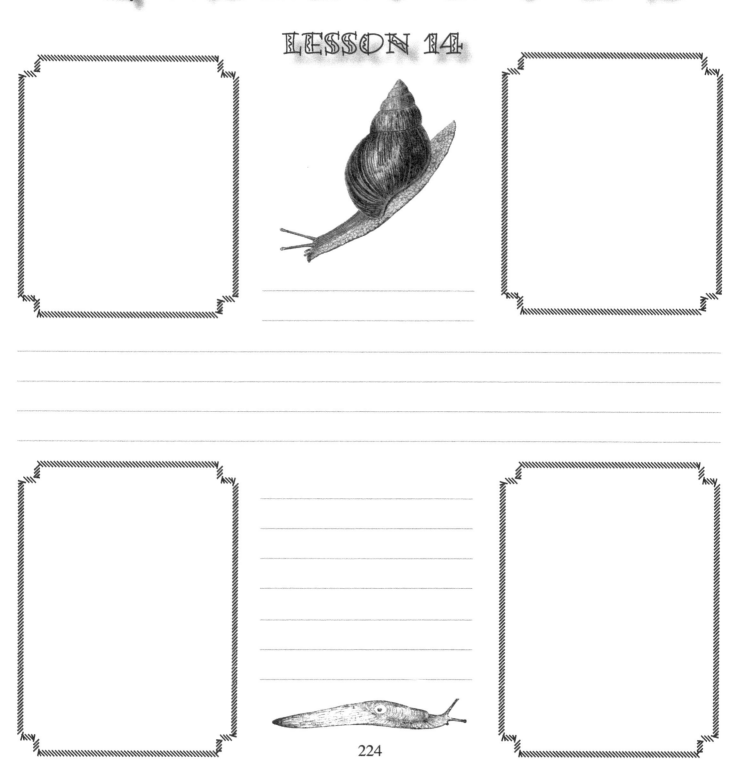

FASCINATING FACTS
ABOUT
WORMS

LESSON 14

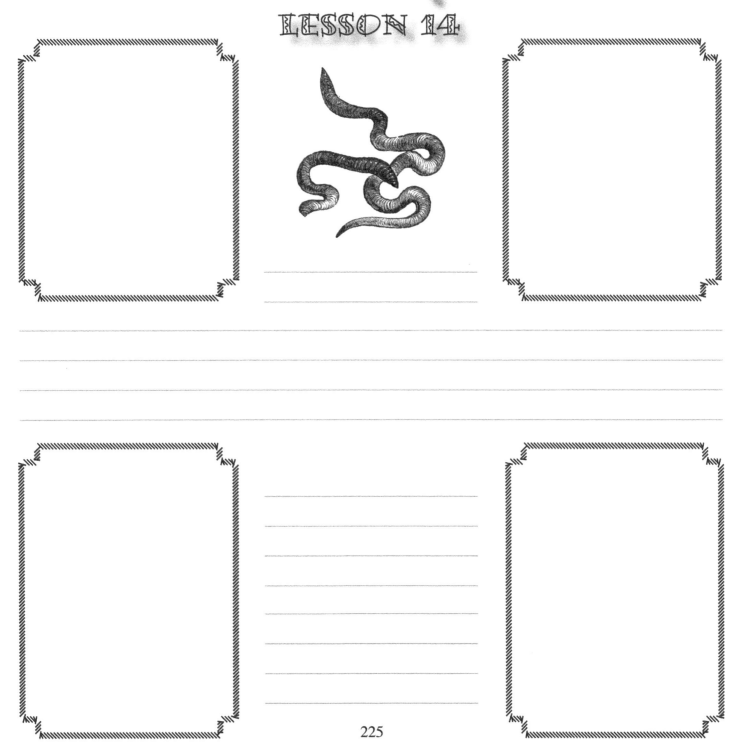

Name _____ Date _____

What Do You Remember?
Lesson 14 Review Questions

1. What are the meanings of the two Greek words that form the name *Gastropoda*?

2. Why do slugs and snails produce mucus?

3. How do slugs and snails eat?

4. Name the three basic types of worms.

5. How does a tapeworm get inside a dog or a cat?

6. Explain the tapeworm life cycle.

7. Which of the three basic worm types are pinworms?

8. What are some ways you can avoid getting parasites?

9. What kind of worm is an earthworm?

10. Why are earthworms important to humans?

11. How do earthworms move from place to place?

GASTROPODS

GASTROPOD ANATOMY

TAPEWORMS

EARTHWORMS

HOW THE EARTHWORM MOVES

Praise the LORD, O my soul, and forget not all his benefits who forgives all your sins and heals all your diseases, who redeems your life from the pit and crowns you with love and compassion...

Psalm 103:2-4

Praise the LORD, O my soul,
and forget not all his benefits
who forgives all your sins and
heals all your diseases, who
redeems your life from the pit
and crowns you with love and
compassion...

Psalm 103:2-4

Vocabulary Crossword
Lesson 14

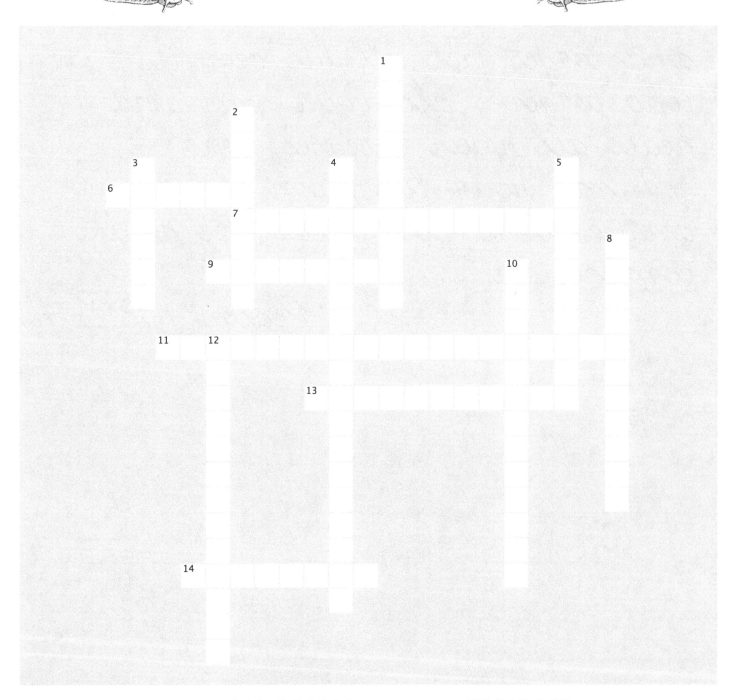

MOLLUSCA   GASTROPODA   ESCARGOT

RADULA   MANTLE   PNEUMOSTOME

TAPEWORM   LAND PLANARIAN   PARASITIC ROUNDWORM

TRICHINELLA   ELEPHANTIASIS   RIVER BLINDNESS

WATER FLEAS   FREE-LIVING ROUNDWORM

Vocabulary Crossword
Lesson 14

Across

6. The gastropod's tongue. It looks like a ribbon covered in teeth.
7. A condition that can occur when the roundworm ends up in the cornea of the eye. TWO WORDS
9. Slugs and snails belong in this phylum.
11. A nematode that is not parasitic. THREE WORDS
13. A genus of roundworm that causes trichinosis.
14. This flatworm can grow up to 30 feet long, winding its way through a person's intestines, absorbing nutrients from the person's digested food.

Down

1. Small animals in ponds and rivers that can become infected with guinea worm larvae. TWO WORDS
2. What restaurants call cooked snails.
3. The soft tissue directly under the shell of a snail.
4. A nematode that lives in a host. TWO WORDS
5. Snails and slugs belong in this class. Its name comes from two Greek words that mean "belly" and "foot."
8. The gastropod breathes by opening this valve and sucking in air.
10. This flatworm has a shovel-shaped head and a flat body. It absorbs oxygen through its skin and has only one opening for both eating and eliminating waste. TWO WORDS
12. Another name for lymphatic filariasis.

GASTROPODS & WORMS MINIBOOK
LESSON 14

Paste your Gastropods and
Worms Flap Book onto this
page.

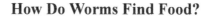

Explore More
Lesson 14

How Do Worms Find Food?

This is an activity for you, not a worm! Set up a maze or an obstacle course in a large area. You can use pillows, chairs, tables, blankets, etc. To get through the maze, you have to move like a worm. That means no eyes, legs or arms! You must make your way through the course to get to the prize–gummy worms! What do you think about a worm's life now?

Create a Dream Home for Slugs

You will need:
A small aquarium (with a locking screen lid) or a clear plastic 4 gallon storage container with a tight lid
Gravel (aquarium gravel or gravel from a home improvement store)
Soil
Rocks and small branches
Sphagnum moss (from a pet store)
A clean spray bottle
Dechlorinated (aged) water, or dechlorination drops
Fresh Vegetables, sliced apples, potatoes and other food

Begin with an aquarium or plastic container. You will need a clamp to keep the lid tightly closed as slugs can push their way out of unsecured lids. Drill approximately 30 small holes in the lid with an electric drill.

Place about an inch of gravel in the bottom of your slug home. Next, add a 2-3 inch layer of dirt or potting soil. To furnish your home, add a few rocks and some rotting branches. Now add enough moss to cover about 1/4th of the dirt. This will help keep moisture in the container. You want it damp but not dripping wet.

Slugs are sensitive to the chlorine that is present in most public water systems. To get rid of it, you can either use dechlorination drops from a pet store, or you can "age" the water by letting it sit in a bucket for a week. After your water is ready, fill up your spray bottle and mist the habitat every day so that it's damp but <u>not wet.</u> Try to keep the slug habitat between 60-70 degrees F.

Slugs need fresh vegetables, and they love cooked carrots! Try kale, bok choy, mustard greens, lettuce (not iceberg), or peeled cucumber. Different slugs like different things so you may have to experiment before finding the foods your slug likes best. Be sure to wash and dry the slug's food before putting it in the home and remove any uneaten food. Enjoy caring for your slug!

DVD and Book Suggestions

Nature: Spiders and Snakes (2006) distributed by PBS. In two episodes, this DVD explores the world of two of the most feared creatures on Earth.
An Earthworm's Life by Jim Himmelman (ages 4-8). A colorful picture book following the life cycle of an earthworm.
A Mealworm's Life by Jim Himmelman (ages 4-8). A colorful picture book following the life cycle of a mealworm.
A Slug's Life by Jim Himmelman (ages 4-8). A colorful picture book following the life cycle of a slug.
Backyard Scientist: Exploring Earthworms with Me by Jane Hoffman (ages 4-12). A host of fun experiments you can do at home with earthworms.
Discovering Slugs and Snails by Jennifer Coldrey (ages 6-9). Describes the physical characteristics, habitats, behaviors, food, and reproduction of snails and slugs.
Discovering Worms by Jennifer Coldrey (ages 6-9). Describes the physical and behavioral characteristics of a variety of worms.
Snail in the Woods by Joanne Ryder (ages 6-9). Details a snail's life from the time it hatches until it lays its own eggs.
Worm Day by Harriet Ziefert (ages 6-9). Mr. Rose brings his science class a cooler full of worms so they can study the animals' characteristics first-hand.
James and the Giant Peach by Roald Dahl (ages 8-12). A magical tale of a lonely boy who sets off on a journey with a handful of new friends: Grasshopper, Earthworm, Miss Spider, and Centipede.

*Be aware that some titles may contain evolutionary content   235

My Gastropod Projects
Lesson 14

What I did:

What I did:

What I learned:

What I learned:

Scientific Speculation Sheet

Worm Temperature Preference

Lesson 14

Name_____   Date _____

Materials Used:

Procedure:

Hypothesis:

Results:

Conclusion:

Final Review Questions

1. What does it mean when an animal has become habituated to a human?

2. Name the traits of a mammal.

3. What do we call the male leader in a pack of dogs?

4. What is a recessive gene?

5. How can you tell the difference between a brown bear and a black bear?

6. Which animal is considered to be a big risk for rabies in the United States?

7. What is an apex predator?

8. Which cat is the fastest runner?

9. Name the three wildcats that live in North America.

10. What very frightening animals is a mongoose able to conquer?

11. What do female marsupials have that other female animals do not?

12. Where do most marsupials live?

13. How many species of marsupials live in North America?

14. What is the name of the marsupial seen in North America?

15. What feature on a primate do scientists use to classify it?

16. What is the difference between apes and monkeys?

17. What is the main feature that makes an animal a rodent?

18. Which mammals are poisonous?

19. What disease do armadillos sometimes carry?

20. What does an elephant use its proboscis for?

21. In what ways do mammoths reveal how the Ice Age occurred?

22. What is a hot-blooded horse?

23. What is a foal?

24. What is a filly?

25. What is interesting about zebras' stripes?

26. What is a rhino's horn made of?

27. How is a tapir like an elephant?

28. What is rumination?

29. Name three animals that are considered ruminants.

30. How can camels survive in the desert, far from water for so long?

31. What is the most dangerous animal in Africa?

32. What features do all reptiles have?

33. What animals are in the order Squamata?

34. How is a tuatara different from a lizard?

35. How do tuataras give us evidence for a worldwide flood?

36. What is the difference between a tortoise and a turtle?

37. What is a frog called before it becomes a froglet?

38. What are some special features of sauropods, like the brachiosaurus?

39. What are some special features of theropods, like the tyrannosaurus rex?

40. Name some possible things that may have caused the extinction of dinosaurs.

41. Which two spiders in the United States are considered dangerous?

42. How many eyes does a spider have?

43. How many legs do arachnids have?

44. What are spinnerets?

45. How is a harvestman different from a spider?

46. What is the telson on a scorpion?

47. What is unique about the bark scorpion and where does it live?

48. On what do ticks feed?

49. What is the radula on a slug or snail?

50. Name one parasite about which you learned.

Vocabulary crossword solutions

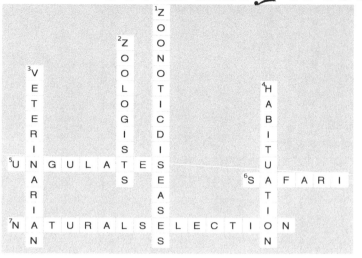

Lesson 1

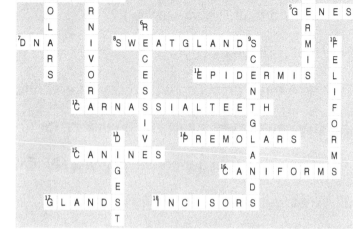

Lesson 2 A

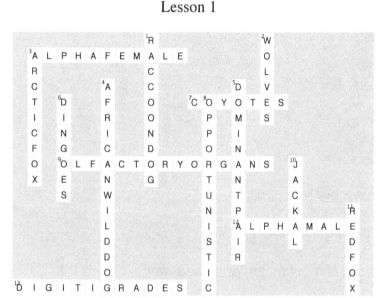

Lesson 2B

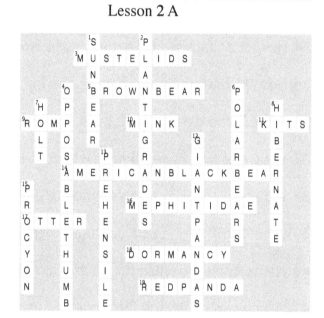

Lesson 3

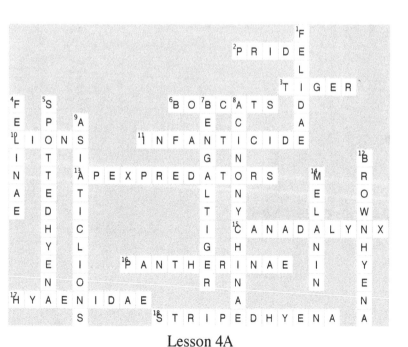

Lesson 4A

Lesson 4B

Vocabulary crossword solutions

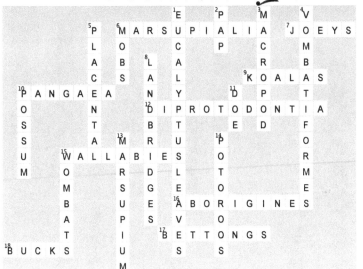

Lesson 5A

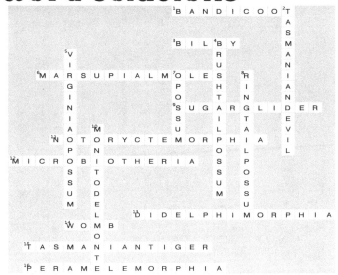

Lesson 5B

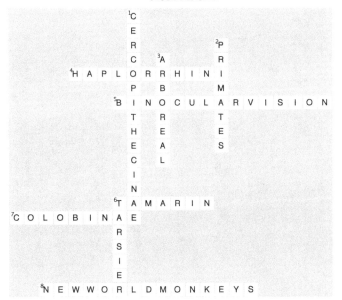

Lesson 6A

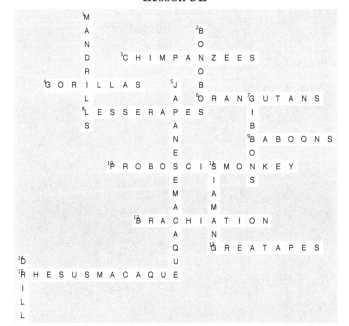

Lesson 6B

Lesson 7A

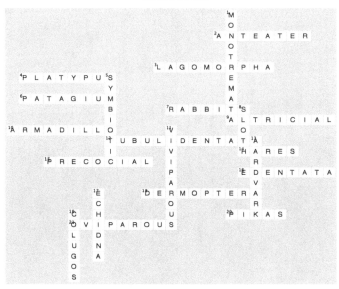

Lesson 7B

Vocabulary crossword solutions

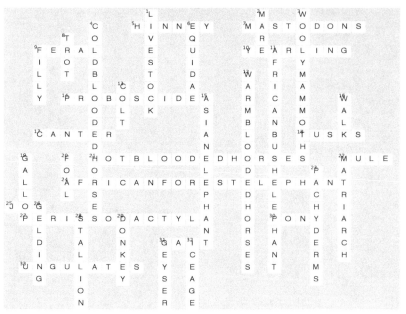

Lesson 8A

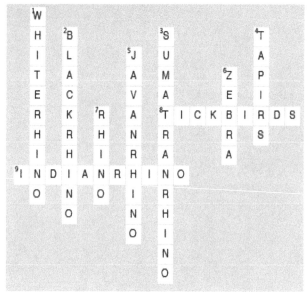

Lesson 8B

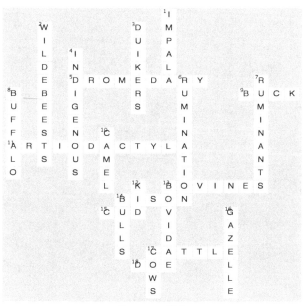

Lesson 9A

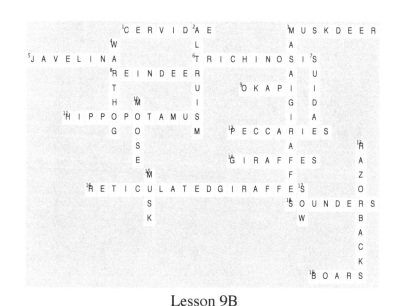

Lesson 9B

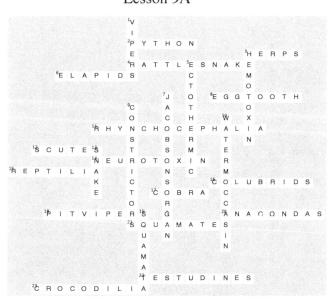

Lesson 10A

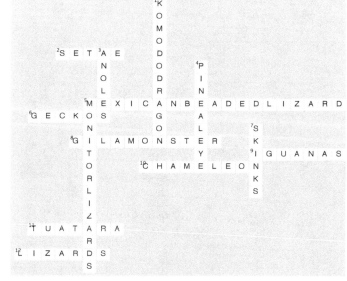

Lesson 10B

Vocabulary crossword solutions

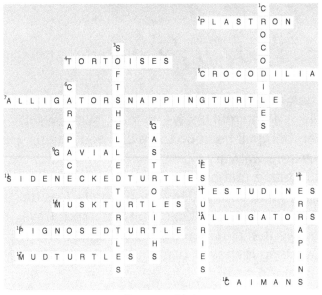

Lesson 11A

Lesson 11B

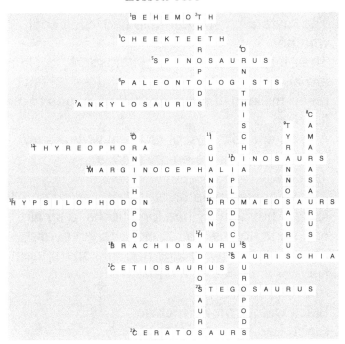

Lesson 12

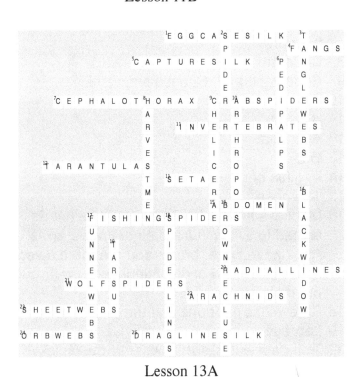

Lesson 13A

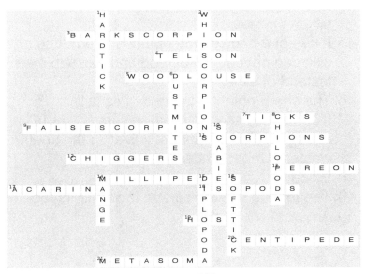

Lesson 13B

Lesson 14

Final Review Solutions

1. The animal has become accustomed to people and is not afraid of them being nearby.
2. Have vertebrae, are endothermic, breathe oxygen from air, nurse young with mother's milk, have hair
3. Alpha Male
4. A gene that does not show up in a person's features. It is masked by the dominant gene.
5. A brown bear has a large hump on its shoulders and is bigger than a black bear.
6. Raccoons
7. An animal that other animals do not consider their prey
8. Cheetah
9. Bobcat, cougar, Canada lynx
10. Snakes
11. A pouch
12. Australia
13. One
14. Virginia opossum
15. The nose
16. Monkeys have tails. Their arms are not designed to swing in trees as are apes' arms. Apes have larger brains and are more diverse.
17. Teeth that gnaw and continue to grow throughout their lives
18. Shrews, solenodons and the platypus
19. Leprosy
20. To inhale water, spray water or dust, pick things up, break branches, scratch, move things out of its path, shake "hands" with other elephants, tear food, smell, defend itself
21. Their stomach contents reveal that it froze quickly before food could digest. Their remains found in Siberia reveal that it was warm and temperate.
22. A smaller horse built for speed. It's not very gentle.
23. A horse that is under a year old
24. A female horse that is young
25. They are unique to each zebra.
26. Keratin, the same material found in hair and nails
27. It has a proboscis.
28. When an animal chews its food, swallows it, then brings it back up to be chewed again.
29. Answers will vary.
30. They have humps that store fat, can drink many gallons of water at once, have feet designed to provide stability on the sand, have nostrils that close during a dust storm and have long lashes to blink out dust.
31. The hippo
32. They are ectothermic, have scales and molt.
33. Lizards and snakes
34. The tuatara has no ear hole and loves cool weather.
35. Their fossils are found with dinosaurs, but they are alive today. Thus, layers of rocks do not mean millions of years but rather stages of the flood.
36. A turtle spends most of its life in water; a tortoise spends its life on dry land.
37. Tadpole
38. They were large herbivores that walked on all fours. They usually had long necks, a small head and nostrils on top close to the eyes.
39. They walked on two legs and had sharp teeth, fingers, and toes with claws.
40. Answers will vary.
41. Black widow, brown recluse
42. Eight
43. Eight
44. The appendages of a spider that produce silken threads
45. It has one body segment, doesn't produce silk, can eat chunks of food and has two eyes instead of eight.
46. The sharp point on the end of its tail
47. It is the only scorpion with venom powerful enough to harm humans. It lives in the southwestern United States.
48. Blood
49. The tongue used to scrape food into its mouth
50. Answers will vary.

Place: Date:

The purpose of this field trip:

What I saw/did on this trip:

What I learned:

My favorite part:

Place: Date:

The purpose of this field trip:

What I saw/did on this trip:

What I learned:

My favorite part:

TRACKIT!

TRACKIT!

TRACK III

TRACK III

Make a pocket by gluing the bottom and two sides of a piece of paper onto this page, leaving the top side open.

Place your Track It! book inside your pocket for safekeeping!

CREATION CONFIRMATION MINIATURE BOOK

(Instructions on back)

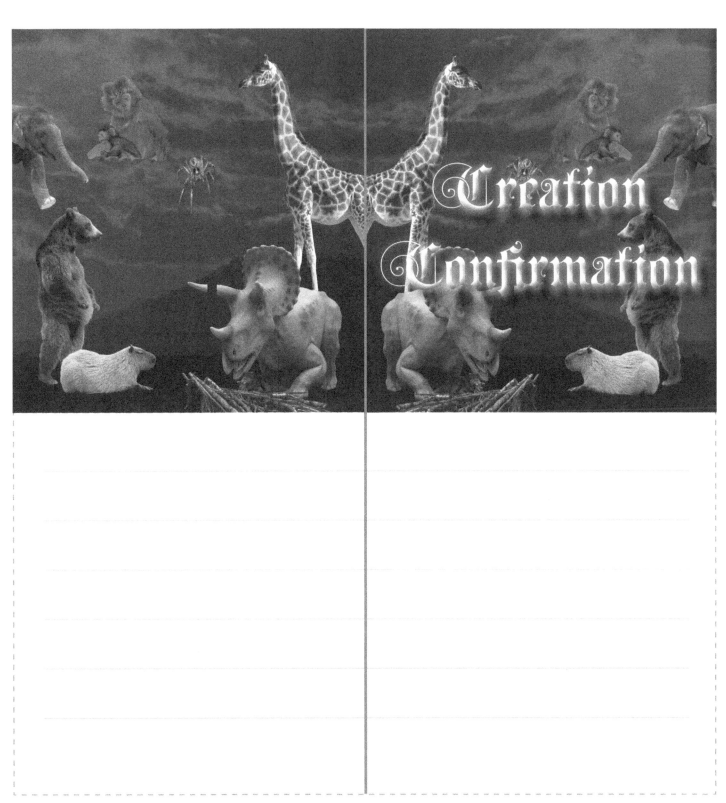

It's important to remember all you've learned about God and Creation in this course. This Creation Confirmation Book will enable you to recall and record all your learning.

Instructions:

1. Cut out the Creation Confirmation Book rectangles along the dotted lines. **Do not cut the gold fold lines!**
2. Fold the pages along the gold lines.
3. Place the pages inside the "animals" cover of the book.
4. Open the book to the middle and staple it along the center.
5. As you work through each lesson of the course, write down what you learn about God, the Bible and Creation.
6. Keep your Creation Confirmation Book inside your zoology book as a bookmark and a reminder to write down the things you learn.

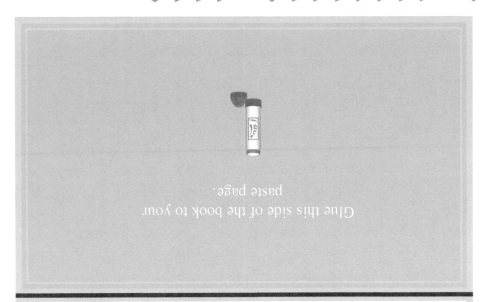

Glue this side of the book to your
paste page.

If you would like to record any additional information about land animals not included in the other miniature books, here are a few extra miniature books for you to use.

Cut out the miniature books along the outer edges. **Do not cut the black fold lines!** Record any additional information you've learned about zoology 3 not included in the other miniature books. Fold your books and glue the back covers of the books onto the paste page of the topic you have written about (on the reptile/leopard print book, choose which cover you want as your front cover and glue the other side to your paste page).

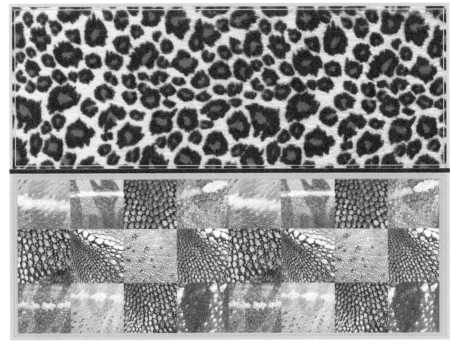

Glue this side of the book to your paste page.

Extra Miniature Books

ZOOLOGY FLAP BOOK

Instructions:

1. Cut out the large rectangle. **Do not cut the green fold line! Do not cut the grey divider lines at this time.**
2. Fold the rectangle along the solid green line so that the words face outward.
3. Cut along the divider dotted lines to create five flaps. Under each flap, write information about the title listed on the flap.
4. Glue this side of the book onto the "Zoology Minibook" paste page *(NJ p. 19)*.
5. Lift the flaps to enjoy reading about zoology!

CARNIVOROUS ANIMALS MATCHBOOK

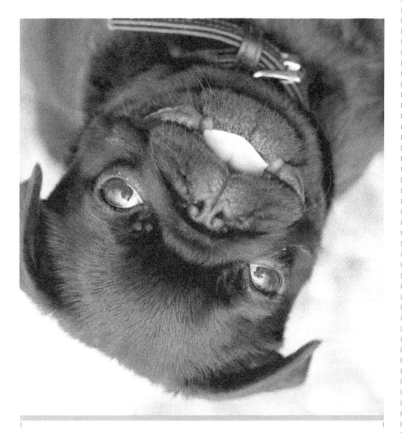

This is the matchbook cover that will hold all your square pages.

Instructions:

1. Cut out the matchbook cover along the outer edge. **Do not cut the blue fold lines!**
2. Fold along the blue lines so that the large dog flap and the small flap face outward in the same direction.
3. Cut out all nine squares on this page and the next and fill in the information you learned about carnivorous animals.
4. Lift the large flap and place all the pages you created under the small flap.
5. With the large cover flap open and your nine pages under the small flap, staple your matchbook on the white line that crosses the center of the small flap. This will hold all your pages inside. **Do not staple the cover closed!**
6. Fold the large flap down and tuck it into the small flap, like a matchbook.
7. Glue this side (with these words) onto the "Carnivorous Animals Minibook" paste page *(NJ p. 34)*.

Mammal Features

African Wild Dogs

Canine Features

Wolves

Coyotes

Foxes

Jackals

Dingoes

Raccoon Dogs

Instructions:

1. Cut out the tabbed rectangles on this and the next two pages. Fold the "Bears" cover page along the blue fold line.
2. Fold the American black bear and polar bear page along the yellow line so the "polar bears" tab is on the outside at the top. Place this page inside the bears cover page.
3. Fold the sun bears and brown bears page along the yellow fold line so the "sun bears" tab is on top and the "panda bears" tab is below. Place this page in the center of the book so the tabs line up down the side of the book when it is closed.
4. Open the book and staple it down the center by inserting a stapler across half the book.
5. Write or draw what you learned about bears on the pages of your book.
6. Glue your Bears Tab Book onto your "Caniforms Minibook" paste page *(NJ p. 48)*.

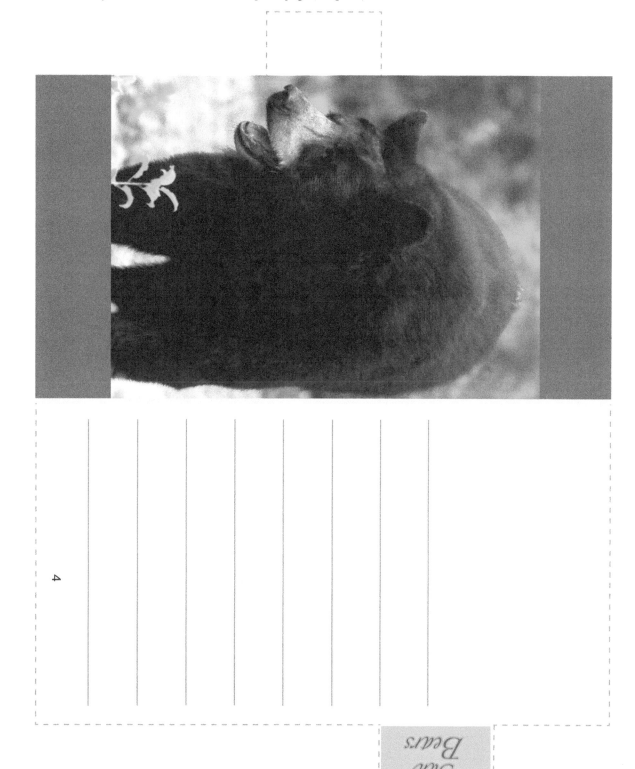

4

Sun
Bears

Panda Bears

6

Bears Tab Book: Lesson 3

8

American
Black Bears

Polar Bears

2

10

Brown Bears

Bears Tab Book: Lesson 3

FELIFORMS LAYERED BOOK

(Instructions on next page)

Stack smaller rectangle on top and line up here

Stack smaller rectangle on top and line up here

Stack smaller rectangle on top and line up here

Stack smaller rectangle on top and line up here

Feliforms Layered Book: Lesson 4

Stack smaller rectangle on top and line up here

Stack smaller rectangle on top and line up here

Lions

Tigers

Stack smaller rectangle on top and line up here

Instructions:

1. Above each title, write the information you've learned about feliforms.
2. Cut out the eight rectangles along the outer edges.
3. Stack the rectangles with the largest on the bottom and the smallest on top.
4. Staple the rectangles along the top edge to create a layered book.
5. Lift the flaps to reveal things you've learned about feliforms.
6. Glue the bottom of your Feliforms Layered Book onto your "Feliforms Minibook" paste page *(NJ p. 66)*.

 Hyaenas

MARSUPIALS FLAP BOOK

Instructions:

1. Cut out the Marsupials Flap Book along the outer edges.
2. Fold the triangular flaps inward along the yellow fold lines so they lay on top of the white square.
3. Lift the flaps and write information you learned about each marsupial pictured on the flaps of the book.
4. Glue the book onto the "Marsupials Minibook" paste page *(NJ p. 86)*.
5. Lift the flaps to remember what you learned about marsupials!

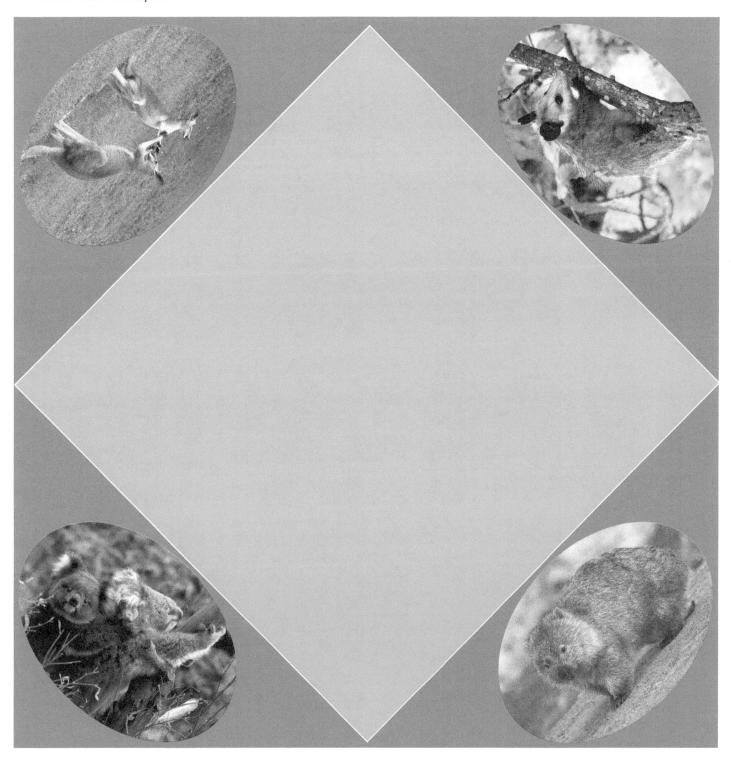

PRIMATES WHEEL

Instructions:

1. Cut out the primates circle on this page. Be sure to cut out the triangular space.
2. Cut out the fact circle on the next page.
3. Place the primates circle on top of the fact circle.
4. Secure the top circle to the bottom circle by sticking a brass fastener through the center of each circle at the pink dots. Be careful not to poke your finger when the fastener comes through the back.
5. Write the information requested in each space of the fact circle.
6. Turn the Primates Wheel to reveal what you've learned about primates.
7. Glue the bottom of your Primates Wheel to your "Primates Minibook" paste page *(NJ p. 106)*.

Primates Wheel: Lesson 6

New World Primates Live Here

Marmoset and Tamarin Facts

Old World Primates Live Here

Primates With Flat Noses

How Primates are Different from Humans

Some Old World Primates

The Difference Between Monkeys and Apes

Some New World Primates

RODENTIA AND THE REST ANIMAL POCKET

Fold inward and place glue along this flap to make a pocket.

Fold inward and place glue along this flap to make a pocket.

Fold inward and place glue along this flap to make a pocket.

Instructions:

1. Cut out the rat square along the outer edges.
2. Put glue along the outer flaps where indicated.
3. Fold the flaps inward and glue the square to your "Rodentia and the Rest Minibook" paste page *(NJ p. 124)* to hold all your fact cards.
4. Cut out the fact cards below and on the next page.
5. Write down information about the rodent listed on the back of each fact card.
6. Insert the cards in your pocket. Pull them out whenever you want to read about rodents.

Squirrel

Beaver

Hedgehog

Shrew

Shrew

Hedgehog

Beaver

Squirrel

Anteater

Aardvark

Colugo

Rabbit & Pika

Armadillo

Sloth

Echidna

Platypus

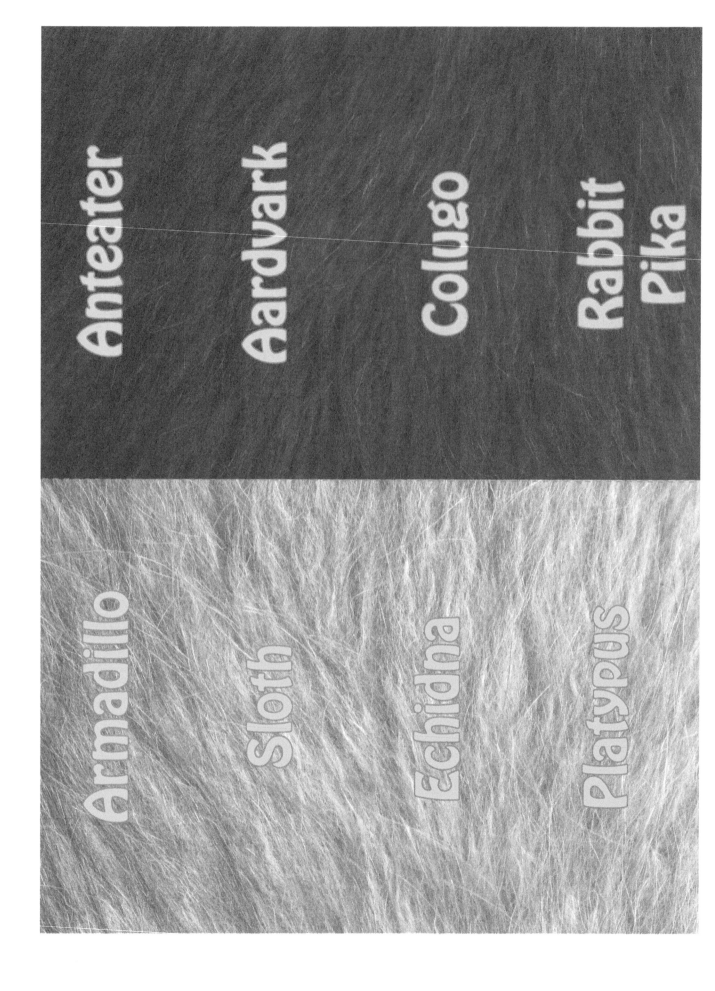

Anteater

Aardvark

Colugo

Rabbit
Pika

Armadillo

Sloth

Echidna

Platypus

UNGULATES MINIATURE BOOKS

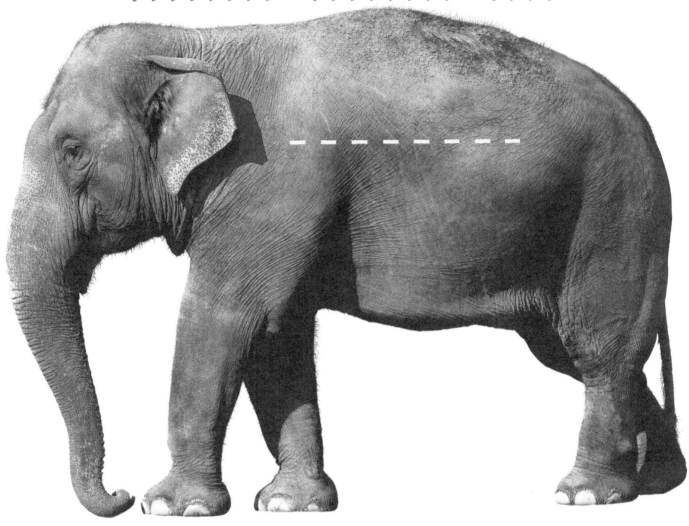

Proboscidea Facts

Proboscidea Facts

Proboscidea Facts

Proboscidea Facts

Instructions:

1. Cut out around the animals on this and the next two pages.
2. Cut a slit along the yellow dotted lines on the animals by poking a hole with the tip of a pair of scissors and cutting along the yellow lines.
3. Cut out the animal fact cards along the dotted lines.
4. Write facts you learned about each ungulate listed on the fact cards.
5. Glue the animals onto the "Ungulates Minibooks" paste pages *(NJ pp. 141-142)* by placing glue around the backside edges of the animals.
6. Insert the fact cards in the slits of each animal.
7. Pull out the cards to read all about ungulates!

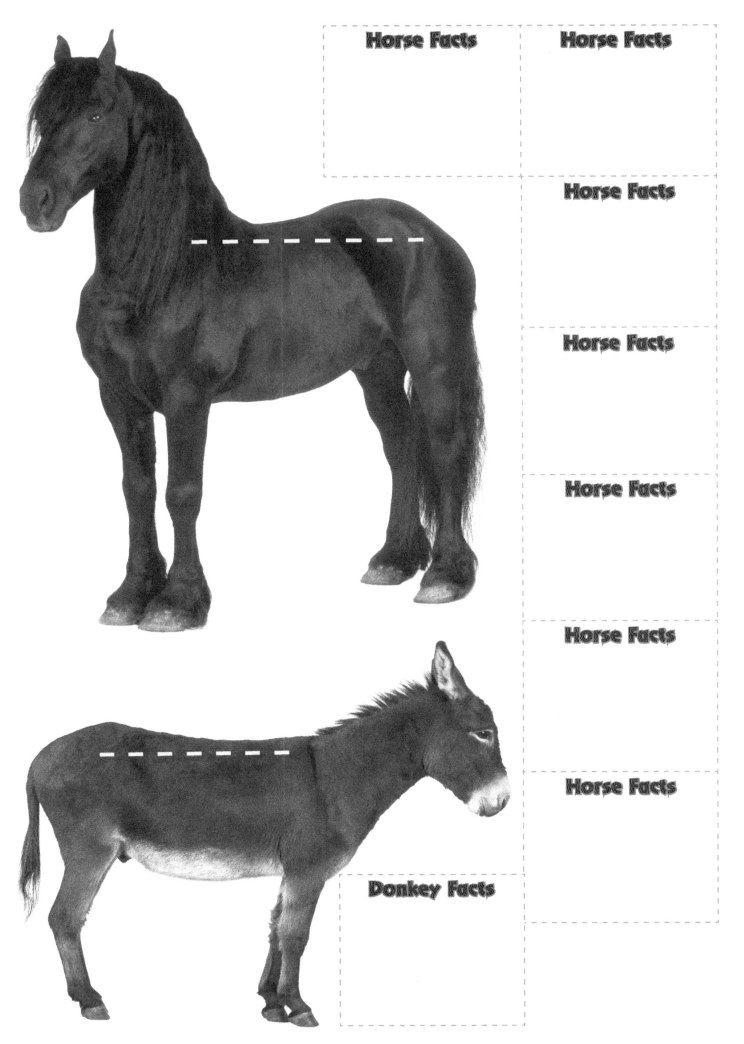

Horse Facts

Horse Facts

Horse Facts

Horse Facts

Horse Facts

Horse Facts

Horse Facts

Donkey Facts

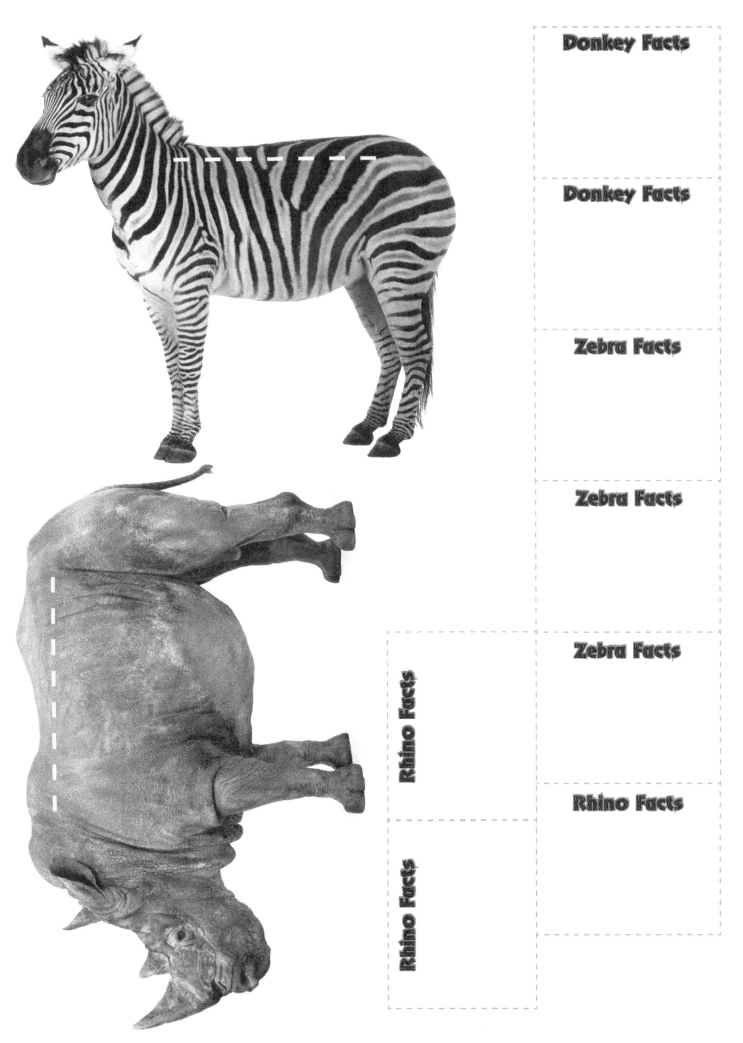

Donkey Facts

Donkey Facts

Zebra Facts

Zebra Facts

Zebra Facts

Rhino Facts

Rhino Facts

Rhino Facts

Rhino Facts

ARTIODACTYLS MINIBOOK

(Instructions on back)

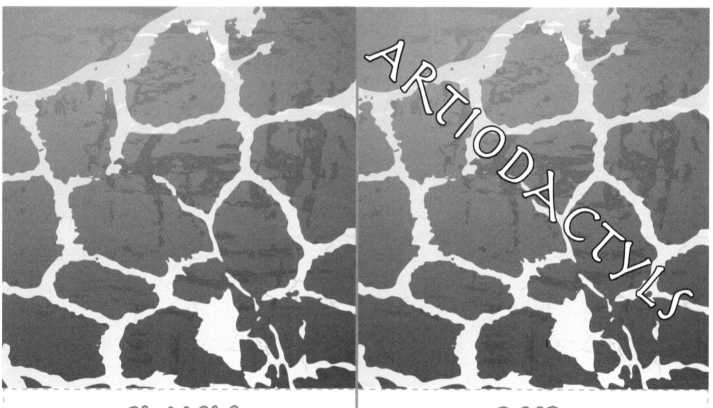

CAMELS

DEER

GIRAFFES

BUFFALO

Instructions:

1. Cut out the Artiodactyls Minibook rectangular cover and pages along the outer edges. **Do not cut the gold fold lines!**
2. Fold the pages along the gold lines.
3. Place the pages inside the "Artiodactyls" cover page.
4. Open the book to the middle and staple it along the center.
5. Write down all you learned about the artiodactyl listed on each page.
6. Glue the backside of your book onto your "Artiodactyls Minibook" paste page *(NJ p. 156)*.

IMPALAS & GAZELLES   WILDEBEESTS

CATTLE   PIGS

SHEEP   HIPPOS

GOATS   OKAPIS

Artiodactyls Minibook: Lesson 9

HERPS AND SQUAMATES POP UP BOOKS

When you complete Lesson 10, cut out the pop up books associated with that lesson from the next two pages. When you complete Lesson 11, cut out the pop up books associated with that lesson from the next two pages.

Instructions:

1. Cut out the rectangles on pages A43 and A45. **Do not cut the blue fold lines!**
2. Write down what you learned about the creatures listed on the lines provided. Fold the rectangles on page A43 along the center blue fold lines and then make four small cuts along the dashed lines in the center of each rectangle.
3. Open the paper up and gently pull each pop-up tab forward.
4. Crease the pop-up tabs with your fingers. Close the books to crease the pop-up tabs along the center line so that they are creased outward.
5. Fold the tabbed book in the opposite direction so that it closes inward, allowing the tab and lines to be on the inside of the book.
6. The covers for your books are the textured rectangles with the titles.
7. Fold the covers inward so that the titles are on the outside. Glue them to the outside of your lined rectangles to form the book covers.
8. Cut out the animals below. Match them to the correct books by the titles on the outsides of the books.
9. Glue your animal pictures to the front of the pop-up tabs inside each book (try to cover the words on the tab - or you can color over the words if you wish).
10. Glue your Squamate pop up books to your "Squamates Minibooks" paste page *(NJ p. 174)* and glue your Herps pop up books to your "Herps Minibooks" paste page *(NJ p. 190)*.
11. Open your books to see the pictures pop up, and enjoy reading all about the creatures!

Herps and Squamates: Lessons 10 & 11   A 41

Herps and Squamates: Lessons 10 & 11

Lizards

Snakes

Amphibians

Turtles

Crocodiles

GLUE THE
IMAGE HERE

GLUE THE
IMAGE HERE

GLUE THE
IMAGE HERE

GLUE THE
IMAGE HERE

GLUE THE
IMAGE HERE

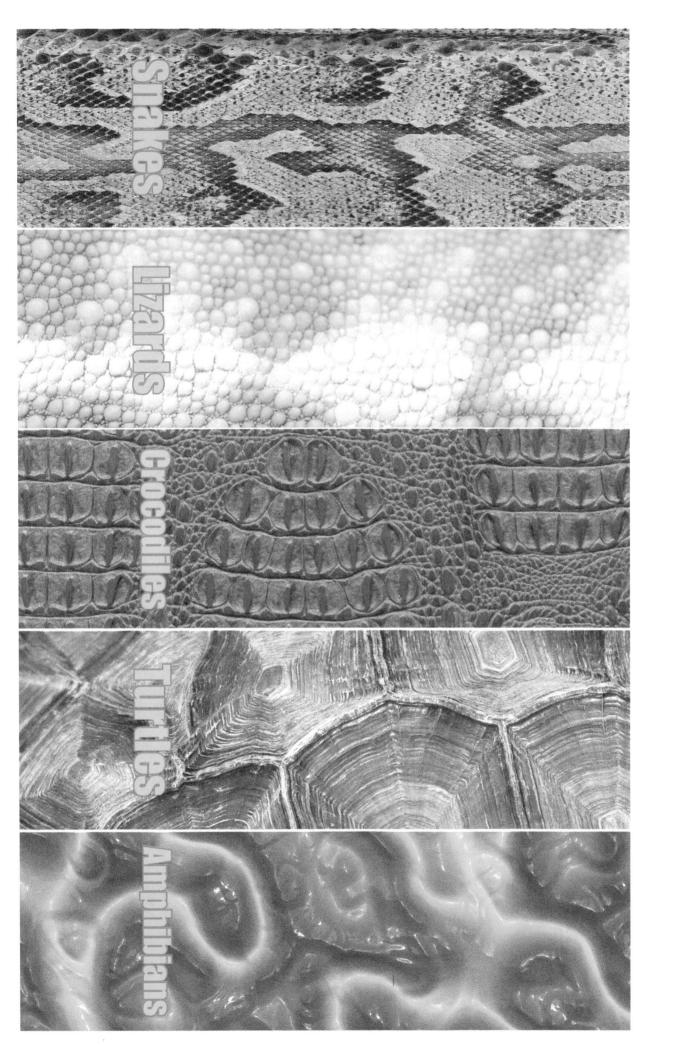

Here are the covers for your pop up books. Fold the cover inward and glue it to the outside of your pop up page.

Snakes

Lizards

Crocodiles

Turtles

Amphibians

Glue this side to your paste page.

Glue this side to your paste page.

Glue this side to your paste page.

Instructions:

1. Cut out the dinosaur books along the outer edges. Fold the flaps inward along the blue fold lines. Write what you learned inside the books. Punch holes on the yellow dots of the flaps. Put a string through the holes and tie the flaps together.
2. Glue your Dinosaur String Tie Books onto your "Dinos Minibooks" paste page *(NJ p. 204)*.

Dinosaur String Tie Books: Lesson 12   A 47

ARTHROPODS FAN

Instructions:

1. Cut out the Arthropods Fan Pocket below being sure to cut along the dotted lines of the outer flaps. Fold the outer flaps inward.
2. Cut out each individual fan sheet on the next two pages.
3. Fill in the information requested under each topic.
4. Punch a hole in the bottom of each fan sheet on the white dot.
5. Stack your fan sheets on top of one another.
6. Secure the fan sheets at the bottom by inserting a brass fastener into the punch holes.
7. Put glue on the bottom and side flaps of your Arthropods Fan Pocket and paste the pocket onto your "Arthropods Minibook" paste page *(NJ p. 220)*.
8. Place your Arthropods Fan in the pocket and remove it when you want to read all about arthropods!

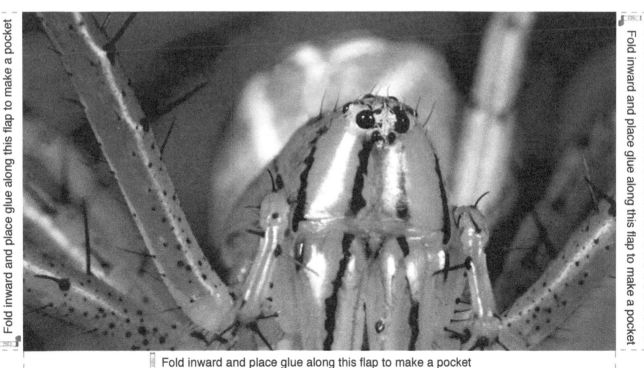

Fold inward and place glue along this flap to make a pocket

Fold inward and place glue along this flap to make a pocket

Fold inward and place glue along this flap to make a pocket

Spiders

Harvestmen

Scorpions

False and Whip Scorpions

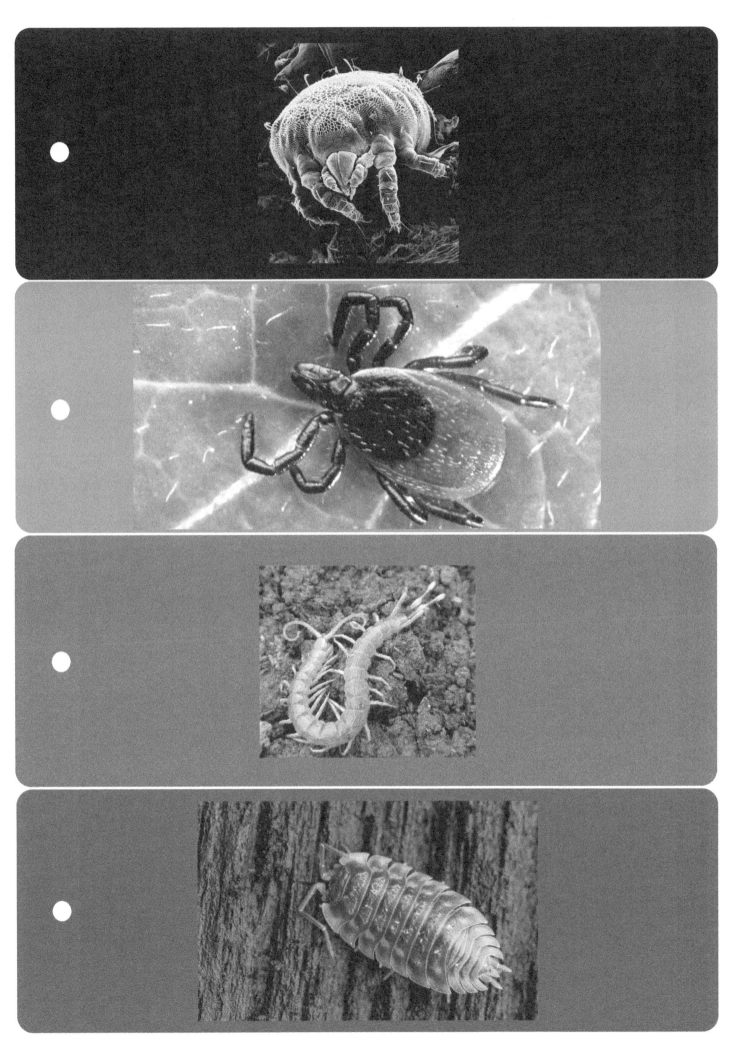

Acarina

Ticks

Centipedes and Millipedes

Isopods

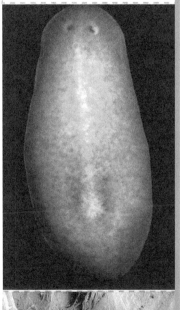

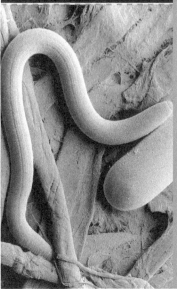

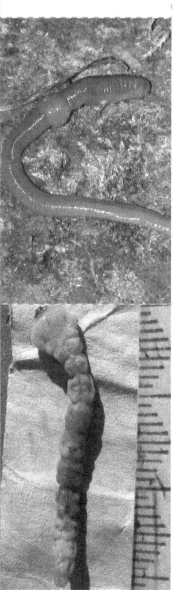

Instructions:

1. Cut out the large rectangle on this page along the dotted lines and outer edges.
2. Cut between the images along the four dotted lines that divide the images into rectangles. **Do not cut into the orange fold lines!**
3. Fold the rectangles away from you along the orange fold lines.
4. Turn over your Gastropods and Worms Flap Book and lift the flaps.
5. Write information you learned about the creatures pictured on the flaps.
6. Glue this side (with these words) to your "Gastropods and Worms Minibook" paste page *(NJ p. 234)*.

Gastropods and Worms

Gastropods and Worms Flap Book: Lesson 14

Lesson 4 Experiment Templates
Cougar Eats the Deer

Cut out the cougars and deer on this and the next pages to use for the experiment found at the end of Lesson 4.

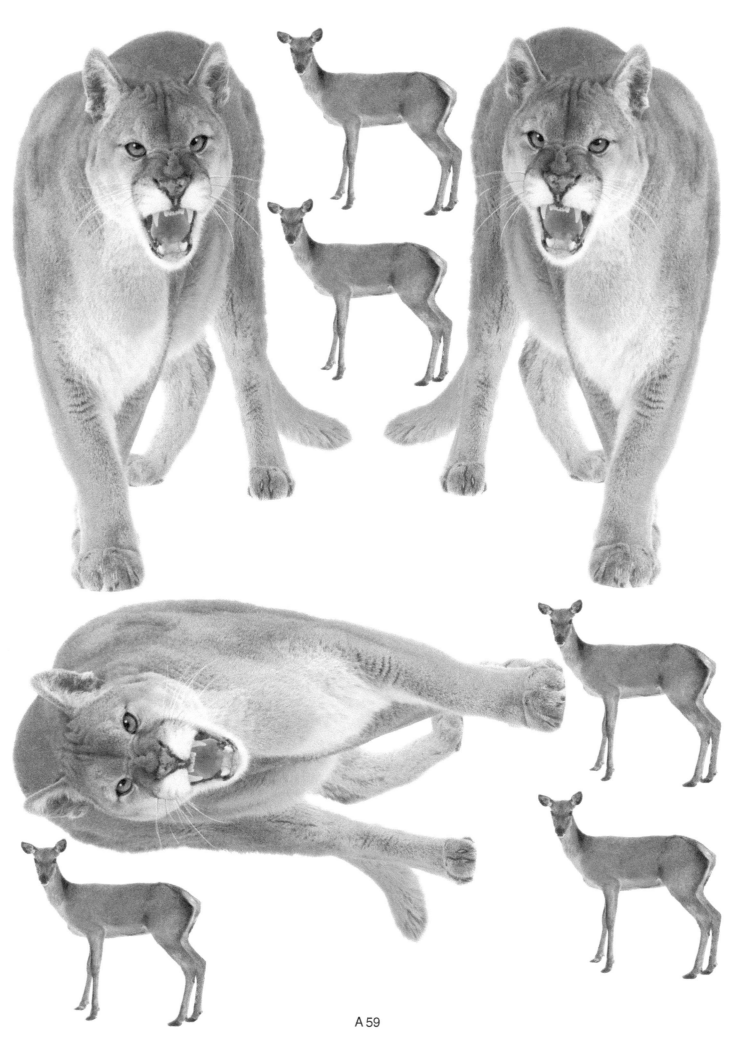

A 59

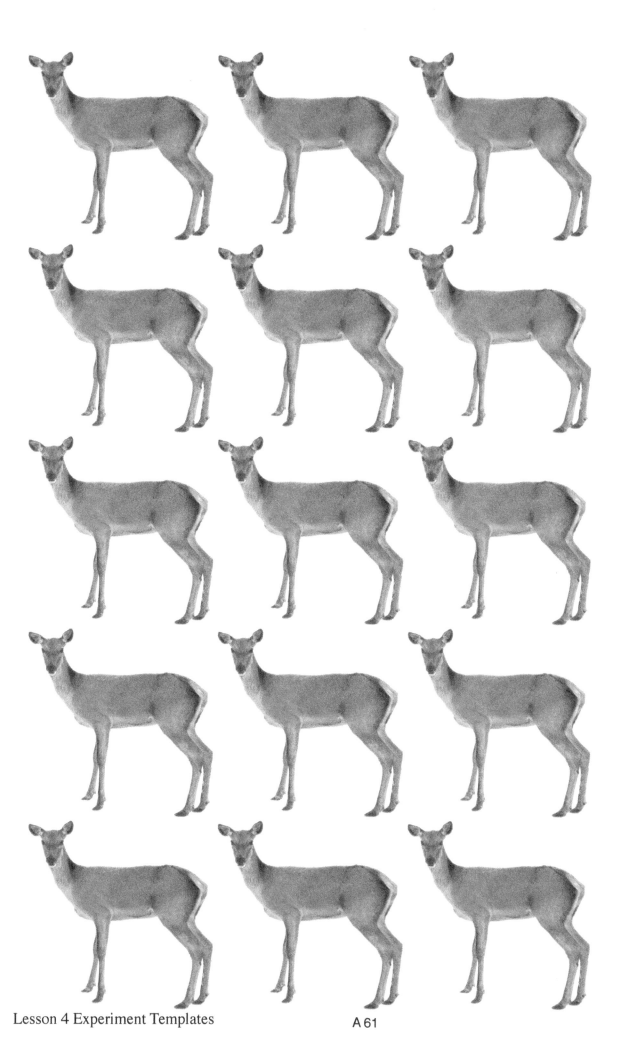

Map It!

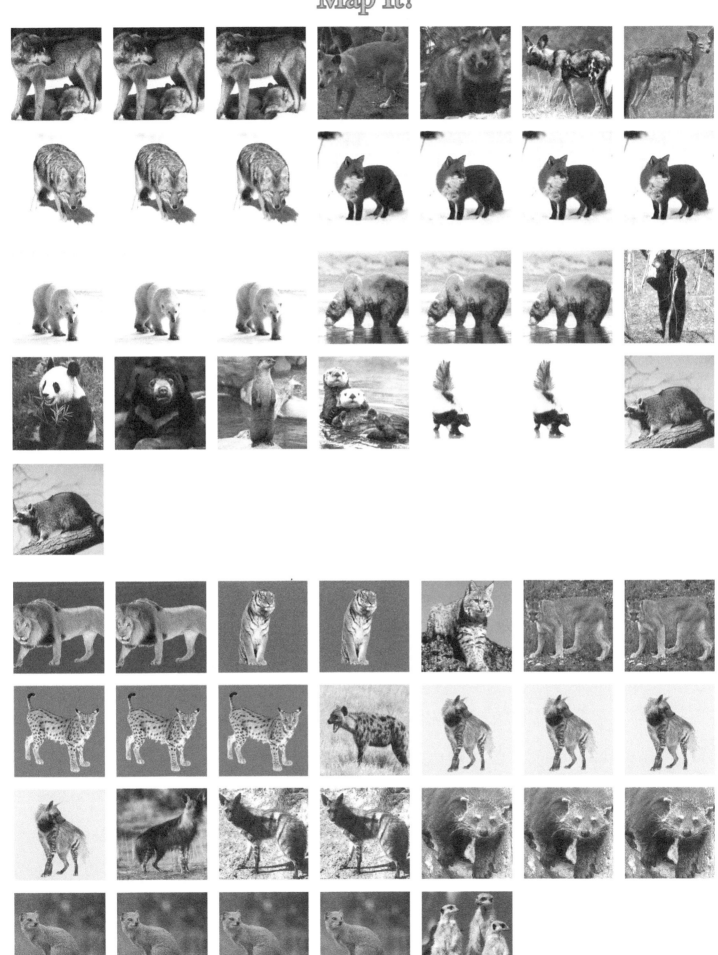

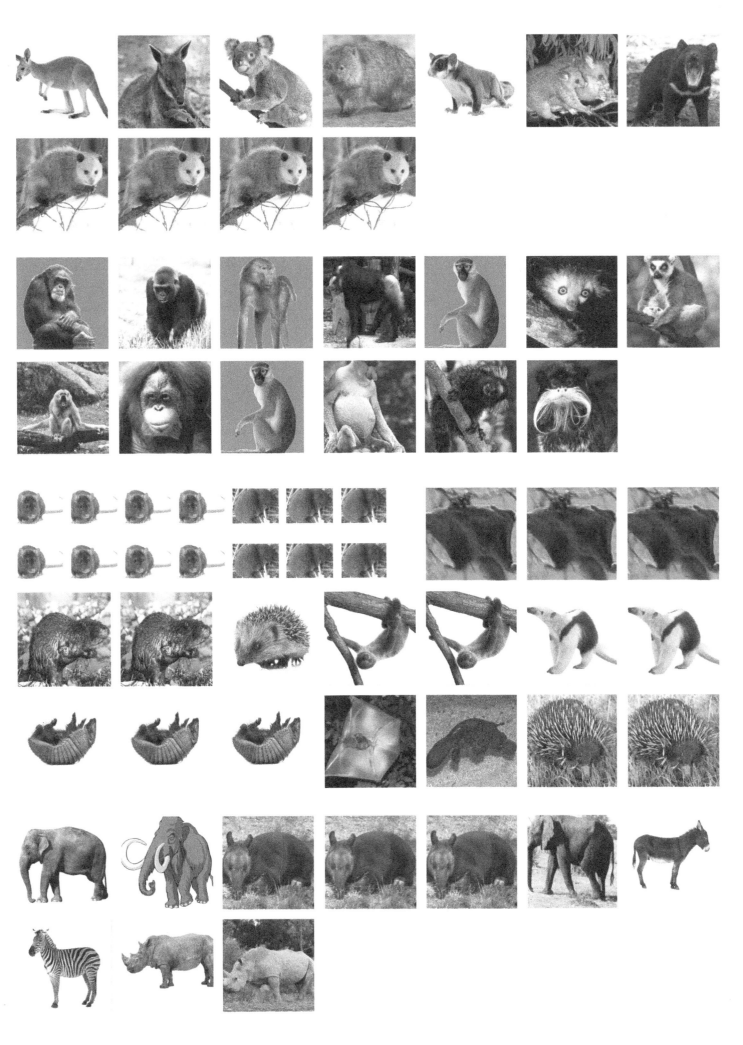

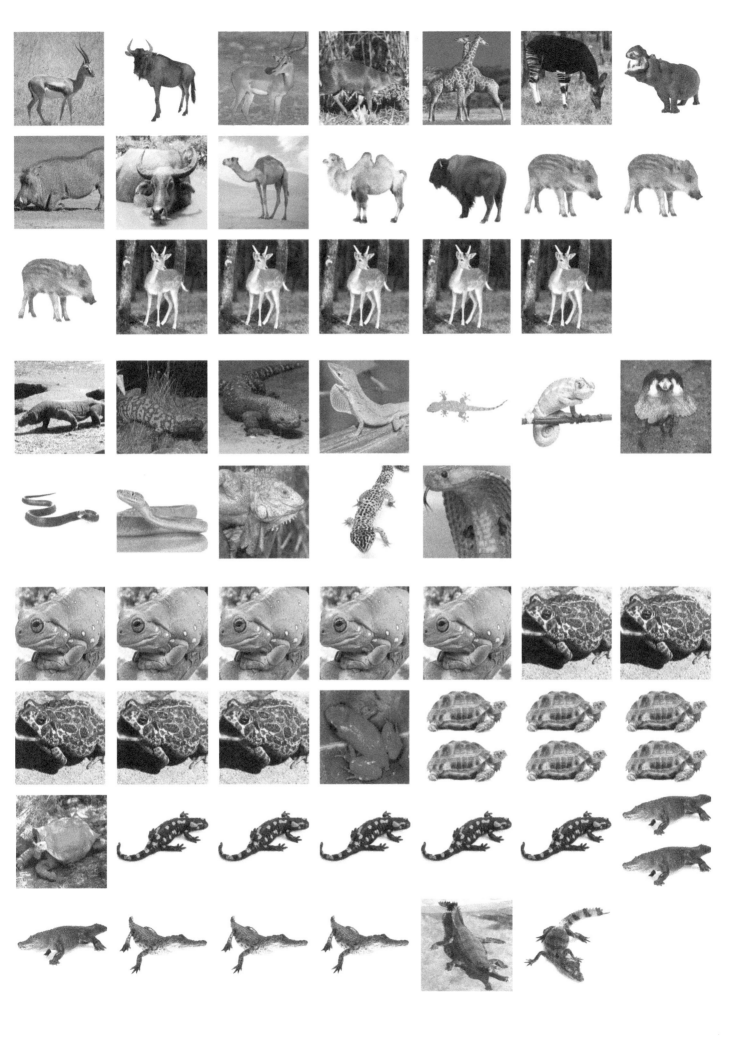

Ceratosaur

Ceratosaur

Ceratosaur

Ceratosaur

Ceratosaur

Hadrosaur

Hadrosaur

Hadrosaur

Hadrosaur

Tyrannosaurs Rex

Spinosaurus

Ankylosaurus

Ankylosaurus

Ankylosaurus

Brachiosaurus

Brachiosaurus

Brachiosaurus

Brachiosaurus

Marginocephalia

Marginocephalia

Marginocephalia

Stegosaurus

Iguanodon

Stegosaurus

Iguanodon

Cetiosaurus

Iguanodon

Cetiosaurus

Diplodocus

Sauropod

Diplodocus

Diplodocus

Sauropod

Camarasaurus

Oviraptor

Camarasaurus

Camarasaurus

Stegosaurus

Iguanodon

Stegosaurus

Iguanodon

Cetiosaurus

Iguanodon

Cetiosaurus

Diplodocus

Sauropod

Diplodocus

Sauropod

Diplodocus

Camarasaurus

Oviraptor

Camarasaurus

Camarasaurus